GREAT RETIREMENT, GREAT SEX

Still
(How to Retire and ∨ Have a Great Sex Life)

I

Writers Out LLC

This paperback edition was first published by

Writers Out LLC, 2012

20 Broad Street, New York, NY, 10005, USA.

www.writersout.com

LIBRARY OF CONGRASS CATALOGING-IN-
PUBLICATION DATA

Larry Gould

Great Retirement, Great Sex- How to retire and still have a sex life

ISBN 978-0-9853330-0-3

Printed in the United States Of America

Acknowledgement

Special thanks to the many thousands of people who participated in the research where their honesty and frankness was in itself an inspiration. Special acknowledgements to Hayley Collins for her in depth research and to Alex Steingold for the editing and research of this new edition. To F.L. who without her love and support this book would never have happened. I would also like to show my appreciation to Inbal Hagag from Writers Out whose help and advice was invaluable; Sue Baker of Lexicon for the many hours of proof reading and her great input, and also thanks to Janet Batten for the months and years of dictation she had to endure.

Larry J Gould

Great Retirement, Great Sex

by Larry J Gould

As Western populations live longer, more and more of us look forward to a long - and hopefully happy and healthy - retirement. But many people find retirement is not what they expected. Loss of the structure and esteem that work brings can start to gnaw away at their self-confidence, affecting their own outlook, and impacting their family and personal relationships.

In this enthralling and well-researched book, Larry Gould explores all of these issues in a frank, forthright and often entertainingly funny way. Everything from understanding the post-work leisure options, to boosting self-confidence, to improving bedroom performance are covered in a highly-readable format.

Great Retirement, Great Sex is a guide through the pleasures and pitfalls of life after work, enabling the reader to plot a course for the retirement they always promised themselves. Whether married, with a partner, or single, there's a wealth of advice on achieving and maintaining a great sex-life, irrespective of age.

Larry Gould is a high-profile British serial entrepreneur and the holder of an Honorary Doctorate in Business Administration. Having build up two multi million dollar businesses with a spell of retirement in between, he knows more than most about the impact that working - and not working - can have on all of us. In huge demand as an interviewee and public speaker, this is his first non-business publication.

Great Retirement, Great Sex is the perfect guide for those planning retirement and an ideal gift for anyone leaving the world of work.

Contents

CHAPTER 8

CHAPTER 9

PREFACE

Why, Larry?

I decided to write this book 13 years ago after selling my business and becoming unemployed for the first time since leaving school at fifteen.

Selling my business was one of the hardest things I have ever done. My advisers said that the acquiring company might ask whether I was willing to stay on, and I was instructed to show enthusiasm because any hesitation might be interpreted as a lack of faith in the company, jeopardizing the sale. On the other hand, I couldn't say that I wanted to stay put, because that might imply the success of the business were dependent on my being there – even though I was desperate to retain some responsibility.

So there we were, both parties assembled at the 'closing meeting', the room was crammed high with piles of paper. Thirteen hours later my adrenaline waned and I lay sprawled across the hard leather reception chairs with my jacket draped over me as a blanket. It was almost over. My lawyer showed me where to put my signature, confirmed everything was in order, and coughed nervously as I read on. "This is your contract of employment with the company – just sign here please Mr Gould." I hesitated, glancing over the crossed out sections dotted around the pages in front of me.

"Congratulations Larry, I knew you wouldn't mind" he says, with the smug smile that all lawyers learn as a matter of course.

I read the remaining sentence of a paragraph which had been otherwise blocked out: "Will be paid at an hourly rate as and when required." They didn't want me, and, worst of all, I had to look unfazed, despite feeling as if I had just been winded. I took a deep breath, steadied my hand, fixed my eyes on the dotted line and duly signed.

I might have been in the money but it felt like the worst day of my life. I made a decision right there and then, something I had been used to doing all my business life: I was not going to be beaten by my new status. I would enjoy my new freedom and make the most of the next phase.

A few months after the sale, I was invited to speak at a KPMG business conference, a formal drawn-out affair with lots of serious people in suits discussing riveting developments in tax legislation. I enjoy talking tax as much as the next man but decided to do something slightly different and entitled my speech:

"How to sell your business and still have a great sex-life!"

So, I told the room my story and talked about how I coped with the wave of anxieties around that time – and how they affected my personal life. The applause confirmed that I wasn't the only one with sex on the brain. I always wanted to write a book and now I had my topic, but shortly after the conference the call of the workplace got the better of me and I put the project on hold.

With the first wave of Baby Boomers leaving the office for the last time I was again reminded of the emotional impact of moving from a busy career - a life where we have a clearly defined role with routine, status, and direction – to the unemployment wilderness.

I considered the difficulties of the transition once more and, with the help of a researcher or two, interviewed many people from different backgrounds approaching or dealing with retirement, and experts from related fields to reveal the most common retirement pitfalls and how they might be avoided by those approaching the transition.

Society assumes that your sex-life must fizzle out at a certain age, but, thankfully, this is nonsense. As we will see, a great sex-life is founded on intimacy rather than intercourse, and represents an intrinsic aspect of your personal wellbeing, boosting your physical and mental health and helping you to live a happier and healthier life, for longer.

If you're looking for a book that promises you the key to happiness, guarantees you mind-blowing multiple orgasms every night of the week then this isn't the one for you, but if you want to know how to retire, reinvent yourself, and still have a great sex-life by making simple and practical changes then read on...

PROLOGUE

A crisis of confidence

IT was 11 o'clock on a spring morning 13 years ago. I sat in a daze sipping a warm cappuccino and waiting for my wife in the plush surroundings of the Harvey Nicks Café on Five thinking about the weeks leading up to my departure, and trying to decide how to spend the rest of my life, when I was rudely interrupted by a tap on the shoulder. I looked up to see an old 'friend' with whom I had shared a flat in London. I never really liked the guy as, amongst other things, he was always a bigger hit with the ladies than I (and too often for it to be a coincidence, usually the same ladies I had my eye on).

"I heard you sold up Larry, congratulations!" He said. I nodded and tried to look disinterested. "So what does it feel like to be retired?" That got my attention.

"I haven't actually retired," I snapped, picturing myself as a withered old man, clambering around for my dentures in the morning.

The froth on the coffee had gone flat, and so had my mood. No-one ever says: "Oh, you know John? He's recently retired, isn't he dynamic? Isn't he sexy?" And now I had joined their ranks, bewildered and ill-prepared.

That was the state I worked myself into by the time my wife returned. "Michele, am I sexy?" I asked.

"Have some more coffee Larry, your cappuccino's lost its froth."

"Seriously, if you didn't know me and we were introduced at a dinner party, would you still find me attractive?"

"Of course," she replied, scanning the menu.

"Michele... do you think I am more sexy or less sexy than..."

"Than who Larry?"

"Than before... before I sold the business."

She paused for a moment; clearly trying to come up with an answer that fell in that delicate gulf between brutal honesty and blatant lying.

"Well, you have seemed a bit preoccupied recently, but, yes, of course you're sexy, don't be ridiculous!"

Was I preoccupied? I've always been preoccupied with something or other, and I must have been reasonably sexy at some point?

What had I done? What had I given up? Do other people feel the same way when they enter retirement? Was I just being melodramatic?

"What about sex?" I said, "I've still got it haven't I?"

"Where's all this come from Larry? You can't expect that things in that department to stay the same. Everything's fine, it just becomes more intimate as you age."

During the next few days I asked myself the same questions again and again; every time I passed a shop window I held in my stomach to look more youthful – it didn't work; at night I tried to be a considerate lover, but I was preoccupied. As well as worrying about my ever-expanding midriff, the word 'retirement' made me think of pill trays and sanitized nursing homes. I had to snap out of it.

Something had to give...

The press coverage of the sale of my business triggered a fortnight of phone calls and emails regarding various job opportunities. Nothing really grabbed me until I received an unexpected call from the director of a charity that worked alongside the Israeli government, air lifting thousands of immigrants from the Former Soviet Union and Ethiopia out of squalid conditions, and helping them to find work and build new lives.

I thought it over and discussed the idea of relocating with Michele and the kids. She didn't take much persuasion, drawn to the prospect of escaping the miserable weather and long working hours of the UK – so it was decided.

During our two years in Israel I met people of all ages and backgrounds, from teenage school-leavers to nuclear physicists. I was passionate about working with those aged 60+ as it was this demographic who often experienced most difficulty in acclimatizing to the change in culture, language and climate; it was humbling to watch them remain resolute in such circumstances.

I realized that those people who got through the tough times shared a positive mindset that carried them through the kind of hardship that most of us will never have to endure. If we view retirement as one of the most exciting stages of our lives; a wonderful adventure rather than the beginning of the end, then this is what it will become: positive thinking is a self-fulfilling prophecy – and nowhere is this more applicable than in planning for and coping with retirement.

CHAPTER 1

JOIN THE GREY REVOLUTION

AGEISM is rife. Greetings cards characterizing the over-60s as silver-haired, docile pensioners with a penchant for flowery poetry should be torn up and thrown in the bin. I'm thinking of starting a protest group for recent retirees, staging sit-ins in card shops and refusing to budge until the last offender has been taken off the shelf and shredded. On my last birthday I replied to every one of these cards with a short note saying thank you, but unfortunately it was heading straight for the shredder. I don't think I'll be getting quite so many congratulations next year.

> **❝❝ If you think of yourself as old, you subconsciously come to accept the ageist attitudes of others.❞** –
>
> *Michael Apple*

"Now that you're retired, you can finall do fun stuff you never had time for! Tip over the trash, chew on the sofa, bark at squirrels..."

The sixth decade of life might have seemed like a daunting and even unlikely milestone to reach a few decades ago; an age where you would have genuine cause to worry about who would still need you and who would still feed you, to misquote The Beatles. But times have changed and retirement marks the transition into a new and exciting phase of freedom and experimentation. To make the most of this time, preserve your personal wellbeing and continue to have a great sex-life, it is crucial to be constantly mindful of The Pledge in order to assimilate the idea that you have every right to embrace retirement as a beginning rather than an end.

The Pledge:

I hereby swear that I will act as young as I feel. I will not be fearful of aging or accept a lower quality of life because of a number; I look forward to the exciting opportunities that each day brings and will embrace my newfound freedom because I deserve it. I will continue to have a great sex-life and never apologize for wanting it, enjoying it or shouting about it: *I am entitled to be happy, healthy, attractive and loved.*

6 6 Kids. They're not easy. But there has to be some penalty for sex" –
Maher, Bill

There is no reason that we shouldn't enjoy great sex as we age. The kids have finally left home, you can make as much noise as you want and experience a whole new level of intimacy with your partner (or take the opportunity to find somebody else, or just enjoy getting to know yourself a little bit better).

So don't be talked into feeling old by generations who find it comforting to pigeon-hole the fastest growing demographic as wrinkled has-beens rather than the energetic, empowered and sexually active people that we actually are.

The power of positive thinking

I remember finding a cleaning job for a 61-year-old former Soviet University professor in one of the new shopping malls on the outskirts of Tel Aviv. I admit that I felt embarrassed as I pushed the contract across the table to this obviously over-qualified man, but I shouldn't have.

He told me that the opportunity to work had given him back his self-respect and this experience would lead to more suitable work in the future. A year later I was thrilled to hear his optimism had

> **" "A pessimist sees the difficulty in every opportunity; an optimist sees the opportunity in every difficulty." –**
> *Winston Churchill*

paid off and he was now working as a teacher in a local high school – positive thinking can change your life.

Whenever I felt those dark thoughts circling I thought about the professor and told myself to get it together. I did a lot of soul-searching before coming to a decision: it was time to head home and take control of my life again.

The path to happiness

I appreciate that this kind of jet-setting is not a viable option for many, and that finance is often seen as the greatest barrier to a happy retirement. While I would agree that money is a concern– particularly when you don't have any - research has shown that it does not play nearly as significant a role in our happiness as you might assume, especially when compared with maintaining a positive mindset and a healthy sex-life, both of which have been proven to boost your happiness, enhance your overall health and prolong your life.

A meta-analysis of 160 separate studies led by University of Illinois emeritus professor of psychology, Ed Diener, looked at the relationship between a positive mindset and a healthier and longer life, leading him to conclude that the correlation was stronger that the data linking obesity to reduced longevity. Diener says: "I was almost shocked and certainly surprised to see the consistency of the data", adding "All of these different kinds of studies point to the same conclusion: that health and then longevity in turn are influenced by our mood states."

One of the studies included was an unusual survey carried out by the University of Kentucky in which 180 nuns in their early-twenties were asked to write two to three-hundred word autobiographies. The scientists returned to the group more than fifty years later to find those who penned positive accounts outlived their more morose Catholic sisters.

Another study Diener reviewed was psychologist Becca Levy's 1975 survey of 650 people regarding attitudes to their own longevity. The results were examined more than 20 years later and again, those who answered positively outlived their gloomy friends by an average of seven and a half years – just by looking on the bright side of life and answering the question "How's it going?" with "yeah, great thanks" more often than "I've been better."

You'll be the death of me

Not only does your outlook affect your lifespan but, as you might imagine, external stress plays a significant role too - specifically when it comes to relationships - with spousal conflict linked to poorer immune response and a decline in health. So if you've been saying, "you'll be the death of me" to your partner for the last twenty years, technically you may have been right. This does not however mean that it is okay to say it every time you have a disagreement over whose turn it is to take out the trash.

A separate study of 10,000 people published in the American Journal of Medicine showed that a happy marriage can reduce the risk of angina and stomach ulcers in men. Those men who felt "loved and supported" by their spouse were at a lower risk of angina, regardless of their age.

REMEMBER: It is vital not to make 'external' factors such as wealth and success the main purpose of your existence, but focus instead on maintaining our most treasured and meaningful relationships.

Shifting our focus towards this goal will alleviate the perceived and actual loss of status, structure and purpose that accompanies retirement as you replace your working life with something equally as satisfying. "But what, Larry? Just tell us what to do!" I hear you cry. The starting point is not buying into the idea that you are no longer entitled to be fit, healthy, happy, attractive and loved just because the number of candles on your cake has reached critical mass.

Positive thinking is knowing that regardless of your financial status or physical condition you can choose the lens through which to view your options at any point in your life; the tough part is having the self-confidence to make the best decisions for you.

Most books on retirement sweep sex under the carpet and everybody knows that gym rats don't spend all that time pumping iron just so that they can admire their honed physiques in the mirror. A 2010 study led by Drs Lindau and Gavrilova showed that better health is associated with more frequent and a better quality sex-life in our golden years. This study emphasizes the link between sex and health in both men and women beyond sixty but gives us all hope that, providing we look after ourselves, we can look forward to decades of great sex – we will look at what part 'the magic three' (your mindset, physical health and your sex-life) play in our personal wellbeing in more detail later on.

The advice in this book is aimed at those of you who feel like you're on the verge of tearing what's left of your hair out if you see one more pension calculator or read about another secret formula requiring zero effort and promising to make all of your wildest retirement dreams come true, because – let's face it – there isn't one. Anybody that says otherwise has got your bank balance in mind, not your happiness.

ABRAHAM MASLOW'S HIERARCHY OF NEEDS:

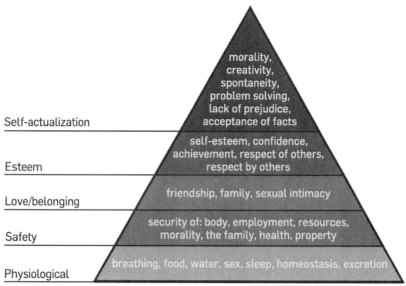

Professor of psychology, Abraham Maslow, developed his theory of grouping human needs into priority levels or 'rungs'. As you can see from the groovy 70s-style pyramid diagram above, sex is placed on the bottom rung (perhaps appropriately, right before 'sleep'), and is classed as one of our physiological needs to represent the fundamental importance of procreation in sustaining the human race.

After preserving our survival and security needs, sexual intimacy is placed on the same level as establishing community and meaningful friendships, grouped into what Maslow termed 'deficiency needs'.

Failure to fulfill a deficiency need makes an individual feel anxious and tense. Although these are not vital 'physiological' effects in the sense that not having many friends or a fulfilling sex-life won't kill you, anxiety and tension themselves are symptoms of a negative

26

mindset which will erode your mental and physical health, and could indirectly reduce your lifespan.

To preserve these fundamental needs I will show you how to:

- Replace the structure and rewards of work with well-considered leisure time.

- Strengthen your bond with friends and family; the most important people throughout our lives – or 'social convoy' as it is often referred to - or focus on finding that special someone if you're stranded in singletown.

- Boost your household income through work or other more creative means.

- And above all, enjoy a fantastic sex-life!

Whether you've always wanted to go sky-diving, trek the Andes, learn French so you can seduce your partner in true Serge Gainsbourg stlye, play the five-string banjo in a bluegrass band or run the marathon with your partner dressed as a pantomime donkey, retirement is the perfect time to seize the moment. However, be aware that because these are the things that you most want to do, the corresponding fear of failure is likely to be great too. The extent to which you let fear dictate your life depends on how much you are prepared to let it.

Susan Jeffers identifies the root of our fears of trying new things as the overwhelming (and irrational) feeling that we just can't hack it. If we work on reversing this negative mindset then the activity will seem far more manageable. Instead of putting something off until you feel better about yourself (which is essentially the same as saying 'I'll do it tomorrow' and putting it off indefinitely) make a stand and refuse to let self-doubt dictate your life; the same applies to your sex-life.

Intimacy and intercourse

It is vital to clarify what we mean by the tiny but expansive word, 'sex'. If you view penetration as the only path to a great sex-life then you are not only placing undue pressure on yourself or your partner to perform, but you're missing out on the point of what it means to be sexual. Intimacy is about touching, holding hands, hugging, kissing, oral sex and everything in between. It is intimacy which lies at the heart of our relationships and intimacy that renews the bond with a partner, even if that frisson of passion has started to fade as our relationship matures.

Housekeeping

Researching this book has been a fascinating learning experience. I am incredibly grateful for the candidness with which all my interviewees have discussed their health, worries, and sex-life in retirement and, although the majority were happy to let me use their real names, I decided to preserve the anonymity of everybody involved in order to remain consistent.

As later-life is often referred to as a second childhood it made sense to begin my journey by rereading my favorite children's story, The Little Prince. The story follows a slightly strange alien prince who travels from planet to planet learning about the strange inhabitants and their bizarre behavior. He comes to understand that the key to personal development and enduring happiness is to form and nurture meaningful relationships and watch them grow.

I want you to grow in confidence as you read this book and feel able to communicate with your partner about sex, and any other anxieties that you may be having as you make the transition into the next phase, drawing on your experiences to enhance every aspect of life after retirement.

Life begins at 40 retirement!

The aging world in which we live means that there is a growing movement of people who reject the ageist stereotypes that words like 'retirement' and 'senior' have come to embody. The old cliché 'life begins at forty' needs to be dragged into the 21st Century: life begins at retirement, because now we really can look forward to decades of healthy and active living and a great sex-life, not despite our age but precisely because of the freedom and experience it implies – so join the Grey Revolution!

CHAPTER 2

OUT WITH THE YOUNG AND IN WITH THE OLD(ER)

The times they are a changin'

THE Baby Boomer generation, the same crowd that sat around smoking groovy cigarettes, listening to Bob Dylan, and vigorously celebrating the development of the contraceptive pill the rest of the time, have found themselves thrust into the center of another socio-economic epoch: the golden age of aging.

Better education, improved healthcare and a steady increase in living conditions have led to a boom in life expectancy. We live in an age where conventional demographics have been turned on their head. The 2008 US Census Bureau report: An Aging World revealed for example that:

- The proportion of people over 65 is predicted to outweigh the number of children under 5 by the year 2018.

+ Life expectancy now exceeds 80-years-old in 11 developed countries.

Unprecedented longevity, coupled with a drop in fertility rates has produced more 'top-heavy' families comprising fewer children and a greater proportion of elders. This means that by 2040, more than one out of every four Europeans is likely to be at least 65-years-old.

You might therefore assume that the shelves of all reputable book shops would be buckling under the weight of tomes on retirement, aging and sex; but aside from the stacks of financial guides (that would be more use prescribed to insomniacs as sleeping aids) you'd be wrong. Instead you will find a busty celebrity's fifth autobiography of the year (surely there's only so much you can say about the changing size of your own breasts?). Apparently not.

As well as enjoying record longevity in the 21st Century, sexually active life expectancy is also at an historic high for both sexes. By 55, men have an average of 15 years of sexually active years compared to 10 years for women. I spoke to many people who still have exciting and experimental sex-lives well into their 80s and beyond.

This discrepancy can be partially attributed to the dearth of sexual studies that actually include older people, with those that do tending to focus on sexual problems rather than normal sexual behavior, and varying widely in their definition of 'sexual activity' – particularly when it comes to masturbation. As women typically outlive their partners and frequently remain single, this omission could distort the true picture of sexual activity in older people.

Increased life expectancy for both sexes means you need to start saving earlier to avoid being caught short in retirement. Gone are the glory years of the 19th and early 20th Centuries where the end of your working-life was conveniently in tune with the end of your natural life. Basically, saying "I'm going to die anyway, what's the point in planning?" just won't cut it anymore.

Money, it's a drag

The reason I didn't want to write a book full of financial advice - aside from there being too many around already, and it would have necessitated hiring somebody to prod me with a stick every five minutes to stay awake, is because studies have shown that money doesn't play nearly as significant a role in our overall happiness as you might think. A survey of 341,000 people published in the American National Academy of Sciences found that happiness dips in early-adulthood, increases in our forties (easily eclipsing our early years) and peaks at 85!

We learn more about ourselves as we age, know who are friends are, have the ability to reflect on our likes and dislikes and, to an extent, are able to steer clear of the dislikes. To put it bluntly, we just aren't as bothered about what people think of us anymore, and this is extremely liberating – a sentiment succinctly captured in the opening lines of the poem, Warning by Jenny Joseph:

❝ **When I am an old woman I shall wear purple**

With a red hat which doesn't go, and doesn't suit me." –
Jenny Joseph

Even if you are a serial planner you have to admit that most of the time things just don't turn out the way you expect; or, to put it another way:

❝ **Life is what happens to you while you're busy making other plans."** –
John Lennon

Wise words as many of my retirees confirmed. Initial responses revealed that many couldn't believe that they were now a 'retiree': "Where had all the time gone?", "When did that happen?" and "What are you doing in our house?" were all questions that I would hear throughout my research.

Despite retirement coming as a shock to many including myself, it was encouraging to hear how many people felt younger physically and mentally than they had anticipated; some of them felt better than they had done for years, and this affected the intimate side of their relationships too.

> **"Age is only a number, a cipher for the records. A man can't retire his experience. He must use it. Experience achieves more with less energy and time."** –
> *Bernard Mannes Baruch*

Our perception of age is relative. I remember thinking people in the years above me at school were 'old' and that my 45-year-old father was ancient, as if he'd been there for centuries like some architectural ruin – needless to say, I don't think that anymore. As with school summer vacations when you're sat at home on the last day wondering how the last few weeks could have just vanished, it's easy to wallow in nostalgia when the reality is that you probably wouldn't do anything differently if you could start over: the same holds true in later life.

Pining for times past, opportunities wasted, and dwelling on regrets will only hold you back. As New Age spiritualists with mystical-sounding pseudonyms like Eckhart Tolle frequently remind us, we only control our actions in the present so it makes sense to focus on the now. They've got a point. Focus on what you have already learnt and how you can apply this experience to a new range of interests and goals now that you are about to retire. Of course, there is nothing wrong with having half a bottle of red and reminiscing occasionally, but putting the past on a pedestal will make you miserable in the present and pessimistic about the future.

Retirement – a dirty word?

Thankfully, times have changed and mandatory retirement in the US is illegal except for certain government-regulated industries such as the FBI, and the United Kingdom scrapping of the Default Retirement Age of 65 in 2011 means that you can choose when you retire based on how you feel instead of when your birthday falls.

If you do opt for retirement you could always rejoin the workface at a later date; take a part-time job; return to education; take up Pilates, and so on. It is the extent to which you can embrace the different facets of retirement that will determine your future happiness.

The Oxford English Dictionary's entries for the word 'retirement' give a telling insight into why even the mention of the 'R' word makes even the most positive person reach for the bottle:

"Retirement: Sport. A withdrawal from a race or match, esp. because of injury."

Retirement doesn't feel like a withdrawal from a race, but the point at which you cross the finishing line and wonder what to do next. Get back in another race! Remain active and if those niggles start holding you back, whispering that you're only good for garden bowls and bridge evenings, think about these examples of four fantastic retirees that are a world away from the bus pass brigade:

+   In 2009 a 97-year-old sky-diver named George Moys jumped with his grandson from a height of 3048 meters (and survived!).

+   Professional weight-lifter and Great Grandma, Winifred Pristell, set two world records at the age of 68, bench pressing 176.2 lb and dead lifting 270 lb —earning the moniker, 'heavy metal'.

+   The oldest first-grade student was a Chinese woman named Ma Xiuxian who fulfilled her life's ambition by starting school at the tender age of 102.

♦ 84-year-old Anthony Smith recently embarked on an Atlantic voyage on a raft made of gas pipes to travel 2,800 miles; according to British paper The Daily Telegraph he even decided to name the vessel An-Tiki (get it?).

Anxiety, fear and even depression are normal reactions to retirement in a society that places a so much stock in youth and celebrity, and woe betide anybody with a grey hair or a wrinkle that hasn't seen Keyboard Cat on YouTube, or heard of YouTube.

Do you want a medal?

The United Nations designated October 1st as the 'International Day of Older Persons' to recognize the contributions of older people and acknowledge the increasingly weathered face of society.

If that wasn't enough, 1999 was named 'The Year of the Older Persons'. Now, call me ungrateful, but dedicating one year throughout the entire course of human history to older people (who are after all responsible for everybody else on the planet being there) doesn't exactly warrant a street party.

In his speech to commemorate the event former Secretary General of the United Nations, Kofi Annan, described life in the 21st century as analogous to a marathon rather than a sprint:

"Marathon runners will tell you that completing such a race depends largely on maintaining a healthy life-style, training and willpower. But they will also confess that there is an intangible element to this often lonely pursuit: that of being in a community of fellow-runners, which can make the difference between fading and finishing."

I wonder if 'Wind beneath my Wings' was playing in the background while he was speaking? If it wasn't, it should have been. Annan does have a point though, and the science is there to back it up. A ten-year study of 1,477 people aged 70 + showed that stronger social networks could have a protective effect on your health and even prolong your life. The study also discovered that it is our relationships with friends rather than relatives which provides this life-lengthening effect, echoing the implied bitterness in that old proverb: you can choose your friends but you can't choose your family.

Researchers think this could also be the result of the positive influence that friends exert over your lifestyle choices - including excessive drinking, smoking and exercise as well as offering emotional support, particularly needed around significant transitions in your life – although I still maintain that I'd be teetotal and thin as a rake if it weren't for my 'friends' constantly leading me astray.

Although traditional social meeting-places still exist, the virtual world has given rise to a 'cyber community' which gives access to an infinite mine of information; strengthens the bond between billions of families, friends and lovers worldwide and gives singles the opportunity to seek new relationships in the real world - whether it's friendship, digital dating or no-strings sex that you're after.

Although a cyber-community is no substitute for spending 'real' time together, it is an indispensable communication tool which bridges generational and geographical divides and widens your social convoy, regardless of finances, mobility and

" Progress is made by lazy men looking for easier ways to do things" –
Robert A Heinlein

techno-savvy. Technology is not to be feared. If your 8-year-old grandson can do it, so can you. But before we open that virtual can of worms it's time to lift the lid on that too often unspoken subject: sex in retirement.

CHAPTER 3

SEX: THE GREY TABOO

The grey taboo

I spoke to many older people about their sexual experiences after retirement and heard the same message time and time again: physical intimacy continues to play a pivotal role in our relationships. The problem isn't that older people aren't enjoying great sex lives, or even that they are too shy to talk about it, but that the voices of those who know are being drowned out by the misinformed general consensus who push the myth that sex fizzles out at some arbitrary age (which subtly increases as they themselves age).

"Is sex dirty? Only if it's done right." – *Woody Allen*

The deeper I probed, the more I realized just how much sex in later life is a taboo, despite the existing research suggesting that older people are enjoying more fulfilling sex lives than ever before. A 2007 study led by Dr Stacy Tessler Lindau looked at the sex lives of 3005 US adults aged between 57-85 and found between half to three-quarters of the participants remained sexually active, with many enjoying frequent and varied sex lives.

A separate study led by Nils Beckman from the University of Gothenburg looked at attitudes to sex in later life and reached a similar conclusion, interviewing four groups of 70-year-olds over a thirty-year period and found the number of participants reporting sexual intercourse more than once a week increased, as did the number of women achieving orgasm during sex and the proportion of men and women who were satisfied with their overall sex-life!

Sexual psychotherapist Dr Ivor Felstein stresses that there is no fixed point at which sexual desire dissipates. The oldest couple Dr Felstein consulted who enjoyed regular sexual intercourse were 91 and 89-years-old respectively and I met couples of a similar age who weren't exactly prudes either...

June and Allan

June and Allan were a couple of expats in their 80s who emigrated from the UK and were now living in Israel. They were a loving couple and still extremely affectionate with each other. Allan had been in investment banking but was recently retired and June was involved with volunteer work, dedicating much of her time to raising their four children.

I first met June while working on an emergency help-line for the Samaritans. We soon became friends and regularly met for dinner after our shift. "Part of the reason we've got it on for so long is the way we are you know, Larry?" Allan says. "We never slowed down. Some couples – even close friends of ours - they grind to a halt after retirement, but we're too busy for that. After I finished working I wanted to stay with it, you know?"

"We always said that we wouldn't be like them" June says, nodding. "The only time we ever had a problem was a few years ago. Allan was worried that he wasn't performing – we're quite open about it – and I noticed that things just weren't happening in the bedroom. We went straight to a therapist – she came highly recommended and we didn't want to waste any time."

"I think the woman was shocked, to be honest with you" Allan says. "She said we were the oldest couple she'd ever seen who were so adamant about having sex. I told her that we were still playing around and both enjoyed oral sex, and occasionally playing with toys."

"It's the younger generations that are squeamish, thinking that we might actually have needs too" June says. "And that especially applies to the doctors. When Allan got his Viagra he said the doctor seemed very uncomfortable hearing that someone his parents' age still enjoyed sex – probably more than he did judging by how cagey he was."

"I had to persuade him to give me more than six pills" Allan says, "how long's six going to last me?"

What made this couple so likeable was that they didn't seem to have the negative voice that so many of us have in the background, telling us that we should take it easy; that we shouldn't expect a great sex-life in retirement; that we shouldn't be so self-centerd. June and Allen weren't embarrassed by sex. On the contrary, they shared a natural, healthy outlook. It was the perfect interview to start off with because, even though I was eager to find out more and ask people potentially difficult questions, Jane and Allan eased me into the process.

The tragedy is that for every 'June and Allan' there are many people who let that negative voice hold them back from enjoying years of great sex in retirement.

Of course, there are many people out there who have never been overcome by their libido, who fill their time with other wonderful and fulfilling pastimes. Nobody should be made to feel 'past it' because their every waking moment isn't consumed by raw animal lust. But, if you're reading this book, I assume you're partial to some raw animal lust from time to time, and there's nothing wrong with that either. A healthy sex-life, as with exercise, or cultivating meaningful relationships, is an essential part of a healthy and happy life.

The birds and the bees II

Talking openly about sex is one of the most liberating experiences that we can share. I'm not talking about proclaiming your private life to the world with a sandwich board and a bell, but of letting your partner understand your needs and anxieties.

> **"The only unnatural sex act is that which you cannot perform"** –
> *Alfred Kinsey*

"But what exactly do you mean by 'a great sex life' Larry?" I hear you cry. A great sex life means responding to your partner's intimacy needs and communicating your own needs openly and honestly. It isn't about the number of orgasms (or even about orgasms at all), the frequency of intercourse, or any superhuman feats of sexual prowess.

As we have touched on, even nailing down a definition of 'sex' can be problematic, as a survey conducted by the Kinsey Institute found out when they asked a group of participants aged between 18 and 96. A fifth of those questioned did not agree that penile-anal intercourse qualified and nearly a third excluded oral-genital contact (otherwise known as anal and oral sex respectively) from their definition. As well as showing that doctors need to tread carefully in not misinterpreting their patients, the survey makes the broader point that the only thing we can say with any degree of certainty is: what different people mean by 'sex' differs, a lot.

A great sex-life means enjoying many different forms of play. This isn't a subtle way of saying that anyone beyond a certain age should wave goodbye to intercourse, but our focus should be on emotional and physical closeness: from paying your partner compliments, to kissing, holding hands and just touching each other.

A 2011 study by the Kinsey Institute at Indiana University gathered information about the sex-lives of more than 1,000 couples from all over the world who had been together for at least 25 years. Their findings revealed that couples were generally happier the longer they had been together, and happiness was also higher in those who scored more highly on a sexual functioning questionnaire. Contrary to what you might think, this contact was predominately "frequent kissing and cuddling" as oppose to penetration, emphasizing the importance of intimacy as forming the foundation of our relationships.

Retirement can make you reflect on your relationship and if you can find even a shard of something left worth fighting for then fight for it! The benefits can be enormous. That doesn't mean it's easy. Living with the same partner for decades can curb the unbridled passion that characterized the early stages of your relationship. This passion is not lost, but buried under years of familiarity and routine. It takes effort to tease it out and dust it off, ensuring that the next chapter in your sex-life is new and exciting, not a tired rehash of those preceding it.

We forget that sex is, above all, about enjoyment – particularly once pregnancy is no longer a consideration. To enjoy a deeper level of intimacy with your partner you have to draw on this bank of accumulated experience to enhance your play rather than fall back on old habits and bore yourself silly.

Where do I start?

If you spend every night curled up in front of the TV with a glass of wine until one of you drifts off and snores like a tractor then it's unlikely that the same environment will trigger passionate sex the following night. The associations that we attach to our surroundings subliminally impact on our mood and on our behaviours.

There are many ways that you can address this issue without spending a fortune but you will have to make an effort to seduce your partner. Remember the three golden rules:

+ Small gestures make a big difference

+ A change of scenery can change your life

+ Step out of your comfort zone. If you don't consider yourself a particularly romantic person and scattering the bed with rose petals seems nauseatingly cheesy then GREAT – do it anyway. This apprehensiveness is a sign that you're stepping out of your comfort zone and acting out of character: change is a powerful aphrodisiac.

If you're struggling for ides here's seven to get your sex-life sizzling:

+ Set a weekly 'date night' and book a restaurant that you've never been to before. Make sure that you are not interrupted, disconnect your phone and reconnect with what attracted you to your partner in the first place.

+ Be more affectionate – hold hands with your partner, offer to give them a massage. Affection shouldn't be limited to special occasions.

+ Tidy the house as a surprise – this doesn't sound too romantic, but if you tidy the house as infrequently as I do, believe me, it will come as a nice surprise.

+ Buy a pair of tickets to the theatre or a music concert (especially if it's somebody you can't stand). This shows you are willing to make sacrifices, and there is no nobler sacrifice than giving up two hours of your life to see Cliff Richard.

+ Book a long weekend away - if you can't afford to go abroad stay in a hotel, you don't even have to leave the room.

+ Buy yourself some sexy underwear to get your partner's pulse racing – this applies to men and women – tattered old boxers aren't sexy.

+ Make breakfast in bed, and try something a little more refined than kippers.

Although this advice overlooks the growing number of retirees affected by the 20% spike in divorce rates in those over 50 throughout the last decade, the statistic that there are three times the number of female widows than male widowers, and those people who are just happier being single – this doesn't spell the end of your sex-life either.

The person who understands your intimacy needs best and how to satisfy them most effectively is you. Masturbation is a satisfying sexual outlet and to the naysayers who say that going solo is less varied than sex with a partner, I'd ask you to consider the added benefits of self-service:

+ **Reliability:** Your hand can never complain of a headache (although you are running the risk of getting a cramp).

+ **Faithfulness:** Your hand will never run off with a younger arm.

+ **Emotional detachment:** You don't have to pretend to be interested in what your hand is saying afterwards.

> **" Having sex is like playing bridge. If you don't have a good partner, you'd better have a good hand."** –
> *Woody Allen*

MYTH: Masturbation is for people who can't ensnare a partner.

FACT: Research has shown that those who masturbate the most tend to have higher self-esteem, a more positive body image, and ultimately, more sex.

Busting masturbation myths

Masturbation is often executed like a special-ops mission: shrouded in secrecy and carried out under the cover of darkness. Now that you've got the house to yourself try making some noise to add another element to your personal play (lube will help here).

> **"neither the plague, nor war, nor small-pox, nor similar diseases, have produced results so disastrous to humanity as the pernicious habit of onanism"** –
> *Dr. Adam Clarke*

Personal play has been the subject of so much misinformation that it's tough to know where to start. Some of the more hysterical criticism would be hilarious if it weren't so serious.

The persistence of masturbation's fiercest detractors makes you wonder how so natural and pleasurable an act could be the target of so many hate campaigns – it seems that some people have got too much time on their hands.

The slightly melodramatic quote above is attributed to a doctor who influenced John Harvey Kellogg, the inventor of Kellogg's Cornflakes. This seemingly innocuous corn-based cereal was originally intended to suppress the libido and prevent masturbation which Mr Kellogg viewed as an abominable sin leading to serious illness and death.

At school there were the old wives' tales that masturbation lead to blindness, hair palms, stunts your growth and other nasty afflictions. These urban myths no doubt originated, in part, from the dim view of bashing the bishop taken by certain religious sects. The generation who were raised with these beliefs will often attach guilt to masturbation which is especially worrying in later life when you may have lost a partner and pleasuring yourself might be a convenient stop-gap or alternative to other sexual behaviors.

The bottom-line is masturbation is a healthy, pleasurable and natural act that should be enjoyed, not demonized. Not masturbating for most people is the equivalent of eating a sugar-frosted donut and not licking your lips, i.e. physically impossible. Here are some other masturbation facts in the same vein:

- A 1987 study published in the Archives of Sexual Behavior looked at the sexual behavior of 81 healthy men aged from 60 to 71 and found that half of the men reported masturbating regularly.

- It's estimated that 25% of people in their 70s may masturbate although as alluded to previously, very few studies even include older people.

- A study conducted by the University of Nottingham identified a possible link between masturbation in older men decreasing the risk of developing prostate cancer by dispelling harmful toxins.

- Although masturbation should never be reduced to puerile humor, I think it is also worthwhile considering the old saying that "98% of people masturbate, and the other 2% are lying" in any serious discussion about sex beyond retirement.

Facts and figures are one thing, but sometimes I think they're best left to business conferences and financial advisors. I'm more interested in people and one of the ladies who told me her story was a 70-year-old woman called Barbara who was incredibly open about her experiences of love, loss and late-afternoon baths...

Music, sweet music

Barbara met David at a factory in Lancashire where she worked from the age of sixteen into her early-twenties. Most of the girls had a crush on the handsome apprentice mechanic, whose appeal was magnified by virtue of being the only man, aside from the owners, to set foot in the place.

"He was very tall and handsome" Barbara says, "He had thick jet black hair and a dimple in his chin and the most amazing broad shoulders. I remember thinking he was smiling at me, but I was too shy to say anything, I kept my head down and carried on working as usual. One day he came over. All the other girls stared and I could feel myself blushing. He invited me to the movies. I never expected it in a million years - we ended up going that night."

Later that evening David walks her home, despite it being the middle of winter. "He lived on the other side of town and we were both shivering but he insisted – a proper gentleman" she says. "We stopped just around the corner from my house street and he said he'd had a lovely night and lent forward to kiss me. I was completely overwhelmed, but it wasn't like today; I wouldn't have dreamed of asking him in, my father would never have allowed it."

"So what did you do?" I asked.

"We did it by the privy."

"You mean you had sex by the wall of the outside toilets?"

"No, we made love, Larry. It was beautiful and gentle, and passionate too. I remember his arms around me, and then a light going on in one of the houses above. I thought we going to get caught and David had to stop me from laughing. It was my first time; he said it was his too, although I found that hard to believe - it didn't matter anyway."

Barbara's home was still cluttered with photographs of the couple. I notice the wear on the sofa fabric next to Barbara, as if he were about to return from the kitchen with the tea. David had prostate cancer which had already metastasized before he was diagnosed. He died just days after their golden wedding anniversary.

I asked if there had been anyone since.

"Oh no, I'm happy as a soloist these days".

"Oh yes, what do you play?"

She tries to stifle it for a second before laughing uncontrollably. I'm pretty certain I've said something stupid.

"I don't have to rely on anybody else for pleasure when I can take care of that side of things perfectly well myself. I have a long bath, then go through into my room, pour myself a large glass of wine, close my eyes and use my imagination. I can be anywhere with anyone, young or old, famous or somebody down the street. I'm rarely disappointed."

When I ask her if she still misses David, I can see her going over memories of their time together and as she smiles, the wrinkles around her eyes bunch together and she glows.

"Of course, I miss the companionship and closeness, but I've been there and I'm happy as I am."

As she showed me out, she added: "I'm not saying that I never want to play a duet again, but music is music."

Barbara viewed masturbation as a natural way of pleasuring herself both during her marriage and after her partner's death. What's more, she assures me that she never had a problem achieving orgasm – this is not always the case and because female masturbation is a learned response in women, as with any skill, there is a learning curve involved.

One step closer to the big 'O'...

In relationships we seek 'permission' for sexual pleasure from our partner both consciously, and at a subconscious level. The loss of a spouse or the breakdown of a relationship can make it extremely difficult to enjoy guilt-free sexual experiences and anorgasmia -

the inability to achieve orgasm - is far more common in women of retirement age. If you are single it can be even more of a challenge to put yourself at ease and grant yourself this permission.

It is said that the mind is the most important sexual organ for good reason. If you hang on to the residue of guilt following the grief of losing a partner or a messy breakup of a long-term relationship, then both your ability to form intimate relationships, and the way that you connect with yourself will be affected. It can be helpful to follow a simple self-focus exercise to rebuild your self-confidence and reconnect with your sexuality:

Step 1: Make sure that you won't be disturbed, run yourself a hot bath, light some scented candles and enjoy the sensation of the water and bath oils on your skin – this is your time.

Step 2: Touch yourself non-sexually, try using moisturizer and enjoy the sensation of caressing yourself. Focus your energies inward, breathe slowly and deeply, let yourself unwind – don't fall asleep now – relax, feel yourself unwinding - don't get peckish and be tempted to try and operate a toaster from the tub – after twenty minutes, or at the point that your fingers looked like crinkle-cut chips (whichever comes first), step out of the bath.

Step 3: Dry yourself slowly; move through to your bedroom. Try relaxing with an erotic book and if that doesn't float your boat, why not fire up a dirty DVD, late-night entertainment or trusty internet smut? If you're having trouble finding the good stuff just check your partner's 'internet history' and there's likely to be a deluge of depravity at your fingertips.

Step 4: Move on to touching yourself intimately, but if you don't feel comfortable at this point – stop, and don't berate yourself either - this isn't a blame game and it is important that you give yourself as much time as you need.

Step 5: If you have a vibrator or other sex aid then use it; although if you are just starting out than light clitoral stimulation is often preferable to penetration - but this comes down to personal preference.

Repeat this exercise until you can feel yourself beginning to 'let go' and don't be disheartened; you need to hone on in your sexual awareness, making yourself feel more at home in your own body, relishing the climax when it comes and not berating yourself if it doesn't – give yourself time.

Retirement for Julie prompted her to reveal something about herself that she had suppressed throughout her whole adult-life. At the heart of seeking permission for sexual fulfilment involves honesty; the honesty to admit what you want to yourself and to those who matter most. This was something that Julie finally felt ready to face up to after years of denying the truth from everybody including herself.

Rediscovery in retirement...

Julie had a fascinating life and a whole new set of challenges to deal with after entering retirement. "I was a straight-A student, not entirely by my own volition." She says. "My parents wouldn't let me out of their sight until I had finished my homework and my mother had been through and corrected it." She studied fashion at London's prestigious St. Martin's College where she won awards for her early collections and caught the attention of all the right fashion houses. "My parents weren't happy about my choice of career. They wanted me to go into something respectable. I was under a lot of pressure and suffered from severe depression in my early-twenties, ending up unemployed after an auspicious start."

Julie had her first experience with a girl at 18 after a drunken night out with her new housemates in the second year of university. "It might have been just a playful fumble to her, but it felt like an awakening to me - or a confirmation anyway." She didn't embrace her sexuality straight away, partially for fear of her parents' reaction, and partially because of her own fears which ran far deeper; a fear of the unknown: what would declaring her sexuality to the world mean for her? How would her family and friends react?

This trepidation would manifest itself in denial for the next thirty years as Julie decided that, yes, she was attracted to women, but she was also attracted to men, so why shouldn't she have a 'normal' relationship with a fairytale wedding, play happy families and try to keep up with a litter of hyperactive grandkids in her later-years. Early-retirement was the catalyst for Julie's decision to 'come out' after turning 55.

"By that time, I felt that I could look back on my career and my family-life with a sense of pride. I wanted to spend the next stage of my life living the way I wanted to." She says. "I had worked so hard my whole life, raised a family and I wanted to travel and work freelance when the mood took me, or if I got bored – neither of which has happened yet. I have two amazing children and the decision to retire was the first step towards embracing who I was – I had never done that before, not completely."

"Dylan – my husband and I were great friends – best friends. I loved him deeply, and still do. I felt so guilty. I felt as if I had misled those closest to me and eventually I just sat them down and came out with it."

I asked her how things had changed since her revelation.

"I told Dylan first, then the kids, who were surprisingly unfazed - then my mother.

She is still close to her husband. "He is one of the kindest, most understanding and thoughtful men I have ever met" she says. "He's still my first line of support and I needed it after my parents heard the news. My mother still hasn't forgiven me. We didn't speak for three years, although we've made progress recently. I don't know if she will ever fully come to terms with it; I think that would be too much to expect."

And did Julie find love after her retirement revelation?

"I am not attached at the moment" she replies, "But I have joined dating sites and found women who have faced similar dilemmas – some still married and unable to take that final step. I feel like I am finally being me, and if it wasn't for the support of Dylan and the kids, I might never have felt confident to express myself – I've been blessed."

Retirement nudged Julie into action, empowering her to take the step that had always seemed impossible and she had a solid support network which made this life-changing decision more manageable. Although homosexuality is far more accepted as a social norm, otherwise intelligent and liberal-minded people still assume that the older generations are all heterosexual. Retirement can be a wake-up call where you decide that you will finally live the life that you have always wanted and age has no bearing on that.

Sometimes it isn't a major change that is needed to get your relationship or sex-life back on track but just a shake-up of the routine that you have fallen into to keep you interested and excited.

Variety is the spice of life

PROBLEM: The routine that sets in from living with the same person for 40 years can erode your sex-life, rendering it repetitive and lifeless. To retire and still have a great sex-life you must break this routine.

SOLUTION: The best way to supercharge your bedroom antics is to have an affair! I'm not trying to incite mass-adultery, but you need to incorporate this sense of variation, passion and, in a sense, taboo back into your relationship to keep things fresh.

A 2010 study on infidelity by Carnegie Mellon University (CMU) found that those cheating on their partners took more enjoyment from thinking about sex outside of their relationship than from the act itself. This shouldn't concern those in committed relationships as long as you keep things fresh, make an effort, and don't take your partner for granted.

So use your imagination, have an affair, but the best thing to do is to have it with your partner. Just imagine it is an affair. Where do you meet? Where can you have sex (not at home of course)? What would you wear? I have spoken to a number of people in a long term relationship who role play an affair. They say it is great fun, and of course it is the feeling of danger that makes it exciting. One benefit is you go home happily guilt free to your partner.

The CMU study also showed that as a relationship matures women desire sex far less than their spouse despite enjoying it equally, as explained through the concept of a 'cold-to-hot empathy gap' which says that unless we are experiencing a particular emotion, it is very difficult to predict how we might behave in that state. For example, if we are calm we cannot accurately predict how we would behave if we were angry, and the same goes for sexual arousal.

As the empathy gap is narrower for men than for women, men are far more turned on by immediate visual stimuli such as pornography, whereas women generally need to be seduced – Debbie does Dallas just won't cut it.

Internet porn:

MYTH: Porn is a scourge on society, corrupting our fragile minds.

FACT: Most adults are capable of telling the difference between fantasy and reality and don't automatically assume that a plumber coming round to fix the taps will end in a rampant four way (it usually doesn't).

According to the Kinsey Health Institute, internet porn addiction is one of the most commonly treated mental health difficulties. The omnipresence of cyber smut means it is practically unavoidable. You could be shopping for a new eBook, or looking to snag a cheap last-minute vacation when a pop-up box appears: "XXX red-hot sex in your area, click here now!" So you click the little 'x' in the corner and two seconds later the thing pops up again. You close it; it pops up, and so on for the next twenty minutes. The ninth time you think 'maybe if I click the link this irritating box will disappear, besides, what harm can it do?' So begins the slippery descent into digital depravity.

The positive reinforcement, i.e. sexual pleasure derived from porn, means that unlike gambling, alcoholism or drug abuse, there is no discernable downside. Porn addiction is dangerous precisely because it has a coercive power to wheedle into your relationship and build an emotional wall between you and your partner. If addiction does develop, it can divert desire away from each other to a stream of virtual vixens leading to insecurity, potential confrontation, and unintentionally rhetorical questions such as "what has that pert young blonde got that I haven't?" The secret here is that old adage: everything is fine in moderation.

CAUTION: Masturbation can lead to relationship issues if you feel that your partner is choosing it over intimacy with you. Although this can be a warning sign that there are underlying issues to be addressed, there is far less pressure to perform if you aren't trying to please somebody else – masturbation can therefore be a necessity rather than a preference – be careful not to jump to conclusions.

Be positive about porn

Think of porn as an aspect of your sex-life instead of a clandestine hobby. Use it as an aide or as a source of inspiration for fantasy or role-play scenarios with your partner; make sure that they are comfortable with this too.

Keep a record of the amount of time you spend watching porn for a week (via any medium including TV, video, internet etc.). Just like a food diary tracks your calorie intake, so will this exercise reveal the true extent of your habit, and whether you might need to go on a smut-free diet.

I spoke to many retirees about their sexual experiences and difficulties, including whether they used porn and/or any other aides or treatments (which we will be exploring in the next chapter). Although Viagra was often mentioned, Stephanie's story hinted at just how important emotional honesty is in our relationships – even more so at stressful transitions in our lives. This was something that I would hear a lot more about later on.

Stephanie

Stephanie's husband Chris has been increasingly unable to achieve and maintain an erection. After some gentle persuasion, he books an appointment with his doctor who prescribes him Viagra. The results exceed their expectations: "The sex was incredible" she says, "I was worried the neighbors might think someone had broken in – it was as if the frustration had just been building up until that afternoon."

After this brief resurgence in their sex-life, he seems to lose interest again and the same old excuses started to creep back in: I'm tired... it's been a long day... I've got a headache... and when they're in bed if she so much as brushes against him he pushes her away. She senses his agitation and feels unwanted and unsexy. When Stephanie suggests he returns to the doctor it triggers another argument and Chris becomes defensive. Two weeks later she finds a half-empty tray of Viagra at the back of his bed-side locker while looking for an aspirin.

When Stephanie confronts Chris and accuses him of having an affair he breaks down; the first time she's seen him this upset for years. But there is no 'other woman' - he has been using them by himself.

"I felt so guilty for accusing him and pushing him away." Stephanie says. "He had been watching x-rated films while I was asleep."

I really did think I was helping" Stephanie says. "I thought that the Viagra would give John the confidence that I found so attractive when we first met. To think I was part of the problem was devastating. I'd be lying if I said that I didn't miss the honeymoon period, but I didn't want a better sex-life at the expense of our relationship."

John was so relieved that he had finally got this off his chest that their sex-life soon picked up as an unexpected but welcome consequence. It also gave the couple a platform to talk about aspects of their sex-life that they would have never dreamed of discussing twenty years ago.

These conversations are often difficult, sometimes embarrassing, but always helpful: once a discussion has taken place, you will both be in a better placed to work towards a solution.

Titbits

- ✦ Sex isn't ageist; those that have the best satisfying sex-lives in retirement don't consider their age at all.

- ✦ Intimacy and affection are the secrets to a great sex-life, not intercourse.

♦   Masturbation is a healthy and perfectly natural part of sex whether you are single or in a relationship.

♦   Keep your relationship exciting. Share fantasies and set aside time to act them out together.

Don't make assumptions about what your partner is thinking – communicate with each other and then you don't have to rely on guesswork!

CHAPTER 4

TURNING MOUNTAINS INTO MOLE-HILLS

IT would be disingenuous to attribute all sexual problems in retirement to emotional or relationship-based causes. Erectile Dysfunction (ED) and female sexual dysfunction can wreak havoc on your sex-life in retirement, but the worst thing you can do is roll over and accept that these conditions are just part of the aging process. Although sexual issues may often seem like insurmountable problems, modern treatments and access to the right information can work wonders and help you get back on track in no time.

Impotence (erectile dysfunction)

Erectile dysfunction (ED) refers to the common and treatable condition of not being able to maintain an erection for long enough to allow penetration. According to Bupa, ED affects approximately 2.3 million men in the UK and figures published by the American Association of Kidney Patients estimate the US figure as somewhere between 20-30 million. Despite half of all men over 40 experiencing ED at some point, only about one in 10 ever seeks help.

MYTH: Impotence is an inevitable consequence of aging.

FACT: Aging does not cause impotence – although impotence can knock your self-confidence and make you feel older.

Don't accept impotence as a natural consequence of aging in the same camp as going grey or feeling compelled to find out what the weather's going to be like further and further in advance. According to clinical sexologist, Dr Swapan Ghosh, 70 percent of all 70-year-olds are sexually potent and while it is true that the quality and frequency of erections often diminishes as we age, ED is often highly treatable.

FACT: Impotence Australia estimate that 75% of ED in later-life has a physical rather than psychological cause, the most common culprits being type 2 diabetes, high blood pressure or heart disease.

As firm erections are caused by a healthy flow of blood engorging blood vessels in the penis, any problem that affects the blood supply could result in ED, and all the usual suspects apply, including obesity, drinking too much and smoking.

What's more, ED can be difficult and embarrassing to discuss because male sexual prowess is so wrapped up in our concept of 'manliness'. Male bravado, characterized by outlandish bar-chat and disyllabic man-noises like "oo-err", "wa-heyy" or "phw-oarrr" mean that we are conditioned to maintain this machismo from early-adulthood.

Performance anxiety can dramatically impact on the quality of our sex-life and, let's face it, there can be a lot of pressure on the man to perform. Even the language used in discussing these matters is loaded with expectation: i.e. 'achieving' an erection – if you build something up as an achievement then it's no wonder too many people wind up feeling like under-achievers.

To take the pressure off it can be a great idea to set a no penetration rule with your partner for a month – this might not be too much of a stretch for some couples – but stick to it. Removing the sense of expectation from your sex-life and enforcing this rule together can bring you closer in retirement.

It comes back to the importance of maintaining a positive mindset, and having the confidence to go back to the pledge and remember that you are entitled to be happy, healthy, attractive and loved. If problems persist there are many highly effective treatments for ED, some of which you may already be familiar with.

Once your doctor has determined whether there are any underlying conditions precipitating your ED, there are many different and highly-effective treatments, Viagra being by far the most popular. To find the appropriate treatment for you, including information on common side-effects and reactions with other medications, always consult a qualified medical practitioner (the unqualified ones might be cheaper but they're also likely to make you worse rather than better). Here is a rundown of the most popular treatments just to give you an idea of what is out there:

Viagra (Sildenafil)

A muscle relaxant originally developed to improve the blood supply to the heart; its true potential as a sex aid was only discovered when the makers tried to recall the drug after an initial trial and nobody wanted to give it back! Viagra continues to help millions of people to achieve harder erections for longer, ever since its worldwide inception in 1998. It can be a wonder drug to those with physical impotence, but doctors still bicker about its appropriateness for treating psychogenic cases. More recent similar drugs are available, the most famous being Cialis and Levitra. You will probably recognize these names from the spam emails flooding your inbox.

Aprostadil

A drug applied directly to the penis, either via an injection or a tiny penile suppository. The scientist who developed the injection was so cock-sure of his discovery that he literally unleashed the results of his research in front of a packed medical convention. The only downside of the injection (*aside from the obvious one of having to stick a needle into your penis*), is that bruising and tenderness around the injection site can result in the formation of fibrous tissue, tenderness and discomfort.

Vacuum pumps

The airtight cylindrical device fits over the penis and attaches to a pump mechanism which sucks the air out of the cylinder, increasing the pressure and drawing the penis into an erection. To sustain the desired effect, a compression ring – or 'cock ring' in the colourful vernacular – is then fitted. Care must be used while pumping and instructions must be read thoroughly to avoid any damage (to the pump and to your penis). According to NHS figures, 9 out of 10 men are able to have penetrative sex using a pump.

Surgery

Surgery is becoming less common in the treatment of ED and is usually only used as a last resort. The most common procedures are the insertion of penile implant (or prosthesis). Implants can be:

+ Semi-rigid - giving a constant erection which can be repositioned for intercourse and for concealment purposes when out of action.

+ Inflatable - allowing the erection to be produced on command by squeezing a small pump inserted into the scrotum.

As with any surgical procedure there is the cost, risk of infection and other complications to consider before handing over your money.

It is essential to brush aside any embarrassment over seeking treatment aside as not only could ED seriously impede your sex-life, bruise your self-confidence and mar your overall happiness, but it could also be life-threatening. Dr. Geoffrey Hackett found that men who suffer with impotence are one and a half times more likely to suffer a heart attack.

The best strategy for avoiding ED and maintaining a great sex-life in your retirement is to live well, relax, eat healthily, exercise, don't drink too much and definitely don't smoke - all of which we will focus on in the next chapter. Above all, communication and reassurance in your relationship will help resolve any psychological issues which may be contributing to any sexual dysfunction and make your partner feel more comfortable about trying a range of treatments.

Jack and Edna Jones

I ring the doorbell, rocking backwards to look up at the grand entrance of the Jones' home with its Roman-esque pillars and immaculately arranged flower-pots. I'm peering in to try and work out whether the flowers are real or not when the door opens and the couple appears in a flash of brilliant smiles and matching tennis whites.

"You must be Larry!"" Jack says shaking my hand, "Great to meet you Larry – a real pleasure!"

Edna is taller than her husband and very slim, her light blonde hair breezes down past her shoulders and curls up at the ends, she reminds me of Elizabeth Montgomery in Bewitched.

I was introduced to this couple through a mutual friend, Bill Reilly, who manages a health-club in Leeds that I seem to endlessly join, leave and rejoin, each time telling myself that this is it: I'm going to get fit, only to leave a couple of months later after trading exercise for the Jacuzzi, then the Jacuzzi for the bar.

We settle down in the living room with its black leather L-shaped sofa in front of an imposing widescreen TV that you can see your whole reflection in.

I tell them about the KPMG speech and my own crisis of confidence in retirement. He nods along but Edna seems reserved. I say that our mutual friend mentioned that they enjoyed keeping fit and travelling. "He said you were adventurous-types and wouldn't mind talking about the more intimate aspects of your relationships as well" I add.

There is a brief pause; a pause I now understand as the crux which either preceded my swift departure, or the beginning of a story.

Edna looks at Jack giving her silent approval – I seize my chance.

"So tell me - how did you feel after retiring from your business; did selling the business affect your sex-life?"

"Hold on Larry, whoa there!" Jack says. I know he isn't American but every time he talks I hear a twang, it must be the smile. "I think you need to hear things from the start."

"Jack and I met when we were 20, in our final year of university. He was always the action man of the group, always off on some exotic hike half-way around the world or training for another marathon. I found that very attractive."

"I know it sounds cheesy" Jack says, "but I knew we'd end up together. I mean, look at her, she's perfect! And, of course, we had a fabulous sex-life."

"Everything was great until I became ill." Jack says. "I first noticed I started going to the toilet a lot more than usual; waking up during the night and, even after I had gone, feeling like I need to go again. I've never been much of a worrier and didn't go to the doctor about anything unless I really had to."

"Typical man" Edna says.

"My Granddad died of prostate cancer and my father had it too, although he was wise to it and they caught his just in time. I remembered reading somewhere that going to the toilet more regularly was an early-symptom and started to think the worst. I didn't want to worry Edna but she noticed that something wasn't right."

"I went to the doctor, had a few tests, went back for a follow-up and after that a biopsy. For a short time I thought my days were numbered. It sounds slightly ridiculous now, but I even made sure my will was up-to-date so Edna wouldn't have to worry. The results came back and it was a benign. I was so convinced that I was a goner the news didn't sink in straightaway."

"I still had to have an operation to remove the enlarged part of the prostate, and recovery was slow." Jack says. "I'm a natural optimistic but it was so hard staying positive – Edna pulled me through it, there's no doubt about that."

"To move on to the next part of your question, I guess it wasn't retirement per se that was a problem; I always had so many other interests that I didn't have to worry about finding things to do when I wasn't in a meeting or arguing with the bank manager. Recovery was slow and my sex-drive didn't return to anything like what it was before for nearly a year."

"I didn't want to push him," Edna says. "While Jack was ill, sex just wasn't a priority. I wanted him to focus all his energy on getting better, but as he recovered he became more and more frustrated with himself; it was out of his control and I think that's what made it so difficult."

"I didn't realize just how low he was feeling at that point" Edna says.

"I would try and get an erection on my own" Jack says. "I bought a few DVDs to help but they didn't. In retrospect, porn stars probably aren't the best place to look for a self-confidence boost."

"I knew something was wrong - he was so distant and nothing I said seemed to make any difference. I didn't care about our sex-life, I just wanted my husband back. I wanted to feel loved and needed. I missed Jack."

"Once we had talked about it, the problem didn't magically disappear, but a weight had been lifted; hearing that, somehow made it easier for me to relax about the whole thing – if that makes sense."

"We started spending more time together, working on the garden at weekends, watching films together in the evening" Edna says. "It was just about enjoying each other's company and the closeness that we used to take for granted - with the understanding that I didn't expect anything else."

"It was nice, but I still felt as if I had failed," Jack says. "Edna couldn't have been more supportive but I still wanted to speak to a doctor and find out what my options were."

"One of the first things I asked about was Viagra. The doctor said he thought it would help in the short-term and prescribed me a six-pack – it was fantastic. I had a bit of a headache, but it did the job."

"It was the first time we had had intercourse since Jack's operation." Edna says. "It was slow and sensual. It was like we were re-establishing a connection or renewing our marriage vows in a strange sort of way."

"I carried on taking Viagra for about a month and although it took some of the spontaneity out of it, I would recommend it to anybody." Jack says. "Thankfully, as the doctor said, I noticed that I was finding it easier and easier getting an erection without the pills and 9 or 10 months after my operation I was back to normal."

As Jack regained his confidence, he returned to the health club and started getting back into his old routine. This removed, insecure person that Edna and Jack had depicted was not the level-headed life-coach type I spoke to that day. The holistic benefits of resuming a great sex-life really are remarkable to witness first hand and their story inspired me to continue.

REMEMBER

- Don't give up hope! There are many treatments for ED but don't put too much pressure on yourself either; share your anxieties with your partner and remember that intercourse is always secondary to intimacy.

- Sex is a habit. If you have broken this habit, perhaps after the break-down of a relationship, losing a partner, recovering from an illness etc., then it is something that you need to consciously rebuild in the same way as physical fitness.

The University of Gothenburg study alluded to previously showed that both women and men agree that the cessation of their sex-life was most frequently attributable to men; the logical conclusion of this being that if Mr Smith is willing and able to achieve an erection (and Mrs Smith wants to have sex) then the rest is history, or in other words: "if you build it, they will come." Still, the sexual problems experience by many women in retirement can be equally as distressing and should not be glossed over.

Female sexual dysfunction

Female sexual dysfunction in later-life is often due to a complex medley of psychological factors such as a loss of desire coupled with physical changes following the menopause. *Female Sexual Arousal Disorder (FSAD) is a term that came into use in the late 1990s to embrace the range of female sexual problems, sparking controversy as to whether it was coined by the same practitioners who hoped to benefit from the development of a 'pink' Viagra.*

A 2011 debate held at the Institute of Psychiatry at King's College London entitled 'Is Love a Drug?' carried the motion that FSAD has been concocted by greedy pharmaceutical companies to establish a tangible female equivalent of 'erectile dysfunction' for women, and hopefully lead to the development of a lucrative 'pink Viagra' in the process.

Regardless of this ongoing sexual dysfunction saga, there are a number of issues, aside from anorgasmia and desire disorders that can be triggered by the menopause, as a woman's oestrogen production plummets, particularly:

+ Thinning of the vaginal walls

+ Vaginal dryness

+ Uncomfortable or painful sensation

+ Urinary incontinence during sex

+ Reduced desire

Many women find the application of widely-available local oestrogen pellets or creams extremely effective in aiding natural lubrication, reducing pain and improving the overall quality of their sex-life in retirement – although this local treatment has not been linked to the same serious side-effects of Hormone Replacement Therapy (HRT) such as breast cancer and heart disease. And as always, any treatment should be discussed with your doctor first.

Take the friction out of frolicking

For many women vaginal dryness is the unspoken threat that can hamper enjoyment of sex in later-life. The great news is that something as simple as lube has the potential to put the sexiness back into your sex-life.

For those of you worried about the 'application' of lube killing the mood, try not to see it as preparation but as an element of foreplay with your partner, apply it to each other playfully and, again, take the pressure out of performing.

The land of lube can be a daunting place for the uninitiated, particularly when its gates are guarded by moody eighteen-year-old shop assistants who smirk when you ask them to take you through the various options. Here's a brief guide to choosing the right lube for you (bear in mind, I am neither a lube salesman nor a physician, so if in doubt, seek medical advice):

Water-based are the most widely used and, like a high-end Teflon frying-pan, are non-stick and non-stain meaning they can be easily cleaned up, and won't eat through condoms. The most renowned water-based lube is probably K-Y jelly which has become synonymous with the slippery stuff. Other big players include Astroglide, Durex and Liquid Silk.

Silicon-based do not absorb into the skin or evaporate like water-based formulations meaning that less lasts longer. High quality brands can be used with condoms (although they will bond with silicon toys) and they tend to have a silkier feel which can make the experience more sensual and pleasurable. Popular brands include Pjur, ID Millennium and Pink

Oil-based lubricants can cause less irritation than other lubricants for some women; they are heavy-duty and most applicable in specific situations such as underwater, prolonged anal sex, or prolonged anal sex underwater. Be aware that these lubricants will eat through silicon-based condoms and are therefore not the best choice for practicing safe sex.

If the idea of heading to your local pharmacy to pick up some lube is too much to bear, you can also order over the phone or purchase products via the internet at the following reputable sites – for peace of mind it is nice to know that the site you're buying from has stores on the high-street too (and carefully preserve your anonymity when sending out packages):

www.babeland.com

www.annsummers.com

www.simplypleasure.com

Don't let embarrassment slow you down...

The side-effects of medicines that you may require in retirement to treat physical and mental conditions including arthritis, diabetes, high blood pressure and depression is that they can all negatively impact upon your sex-life. It may be that the specific medicine you are taking is necessary in treating a serious complaint, or simply that your doctor has discounted your sex-life fromhis or her diagnosis entirely. Tell your doctor about any unwanted side-effects, voice your concerns and get the information you need to make an informed decision.

Contrary to popular opinion, it isn't just men that are put off seeking help for sexual matters. A study led by Professor Linda Cardozo found that only a quarter of women with vaginal problems ever seek treatment. That means three-quarters are missing out on easy-fixes that could transform their sex-life in retirement.

❛❛Shop around – medicine includes all sorts, and you don't have to put up with a Hippocratic oaf.'' – *Andrew Comfort*

If you have built a rapport with your doctor over the years and have no qualms about approaching him or her with sexual matters then that's fine, but let's face it, it can be embarrassing discussing your sex-life openly and honestly – I should know, I offended enough people over the past few years while compiling this book.

BEWARE: The ease with which a doctor can dismiss your sex-life in his or her choice of medicine for an unrelated condition may boil down to the false assumption that you aren't all that interested in sex (based on their own lack of libido).

Conversely, if your doctor seems insensitive, hesitant or makes you feel uncomfortable then ask to see someone else – don't let your sex-life suffer – particularly if you are experiencing any unusual symptoms such as pain, bleeding or unusual discharge. These are not 'facts of life' or part of the aging process. Many women find it easier discussing feminine issues with a female doctor, if this is you, then again, find another doctor: your health and happiness are too important to leave to chance.

The difficulty with dealing with sexual dysfunction at any stage is that these are not clear-cut problems. Sometimes symptoms manifest themselves gradually over a prolonged period of times.

Sometimes the problem is indirect; something seemingly innocuous that snowballs and turns from a mild annoyance into a relationship-threatening gargantuan mega-problem that requires urgent attention: yes, I'm talking about snoring.

Snoring: the not-so-silent relationship killer

Snoring might seem like a harmless or even amusing bodily function to anybody whose relationship hasn't been pushed to breaking-point by it. The recent trend of Hollywood A-listers including pint-sized action hero Tom Cruise building sound-proof 'snoratoriums' in their homes is testament to the extreme lengths people will go to silence the problem and give their partners some peace.

> **Laugh and the world laughs with you, snore and you sleep alone"** –
> *Anthony Burgess*

Although the amount of sleep we need typically decreases with age, sleep deprivation is also a form of torture. You wouldn't find it funny if your partner set up an elaborate funnel system above the bed to drip water onto your forehead throughout the night – but this is exactly what snoring is, only replace water drips with grunts that in the case of one of the world's loudest snorers, Jenny Chapman, can reach a volume of 111.6 dB – louder than a low-flying jet.

A study of more than 1,000 unlucky partners of prolific snorers carried out by the British Association of Snoring and Sleep Apnea, revealed that long-suffering spouses are kept awake for two hours a night, adding up to two years of lost sleep over the course of an average marriage - and the same amount of time fighting the urge to smother your dearly beloved with a pillow. More than 80 percent of the participants said snoring was adversely affecting their relationship, with the majority of spouses agreeing that it had harmed their sex-life.

And it's not just your sex-life that could suffer but your general health too. A 2008 study led by scientists from Imperial College London monitored the physical effects of living in a noisy area (under the flight path of London's Heathrow airport) on a group of 140 people while they slept. The results showed that exposure to any noise above 35 dB during sleep can significantly raise your blood pressure. In other words, your partner's rattling could be hazardous to your health.

If you are advised to temporarily abstain to aid recovery from an operation ask if this is essential to your recovery or just an overly-cautious formality. For example, after a vasectomy, it is usually advised that you shouldn't have sex for at least a week and heart-attack sufferers are often told to take a four to six week break for good reason (although I can think of worse ways to go).

Snoring solutions

As snoring is the result of an airway obstruction causing irregular airflow during sleep, the majority of treatments are targeted at clearing this obstruction. The right treatment for you depends on the cause of the blockage, as determined by a medical professional. Snoring can be triggered by myriad factors including smoking and being excessively overweight, and treatment varies from nasal sprays and strips for a blocked nose; to thyroxin, if you're diagnosed with an underactive thyroid (hypothyroidism); right up to various breathing apparatus and invasive operations to treat sleep apnea.

I met my next interviewee on a snoring/sleep apnea related internet forum. I stumbled across a user called Liz who started a thread originally seeking advice to help deal with her husband's snoring, before sharing her knowledge with others who had taken to the internet in desperation.

Harry and Liz were fast approaching their Ruby wedding anniversary but didn't feel much like celebrating. The problems all started around the same time that Harry, a rotund and red-faced retired teacher started snoring. "He's always snored a little bit – I'm sure we all do sometimes" Liz says, "but this was something else – a different league, honestly you've never heard anything like it – a strange spluttering, almost gagging sound. At first I tried to ignore it - I'd prod him and call his name to wake him up so I could try and get to sleep before he started up again."

"I've never been a morning person" Harry says, "I always used to wake up shattered and stay like that all day. Liz seemed off with me until about lunchtime after a bad night and, to be honest I thought she was probably being a little over the top about the situation anyway."

"I knew it wasn't his fault" Liz says, "but it's difficult not to snap when all you want is a decent night's sleep – I was still working part-time as a payroll assistant and couldn't concentrate; I was making silly mistakes. I tried turning the other way around, so that my head was parallel with his feet, but it wasn't far enough away to make a difference and being so close to Harry's feet carried its own drawbacks. Next I tried earplugs which reduced the noise but were uncomfortable and didn't really help either..."

"I started looking for advice on the internet and about half an hour in I spotted a message from someone saying that snoring can be a sign of more serious underlying health problems. I had been so busy concentrating on my lack of energy and trying to find a way around it that I didn't really think about Harry – I felt terrible."

"I told her that if it was bothering her that much, I could move into the spare room for a while and in the mean-time I'd see the doctor." Harry says. "It had reached the point where it was a daily source of arguments and we were both ready to do something about it."

"I didn't want to feel like a nag, especially over something that Harry couldn't help" but I was relieved to hear him say that – to know that we might actually be able to sort things out."

I asked how the new sleeping arrangement worked out for them and whether snoring had had a detrimental impact on their sex-life. After answering the question the expression on Liz's face told me that I had hit the nail on the head. She explained that a lack of sleep had not only impacted her work, but left her libido in tatters. Her husband's snoring meant that bedtime had become about getting as far away from each other as possible and intimacy was the last thing on her mind.

"We reached a compromise" Liz says. "The first night Harry moved into the spare room, I agreed to stay with him until he fell asleep and then make my way back into our bedroom. That's when we started seeing the funny side of the situation. We were lying in bed and I was telling him to hurry up and get to sleep so I could leave. We ended up having sex for the first time in months, and not just once. You don't realize how bad things have got until they start getting better and that night was the turning-point. And surprise, surprise, Harry had not trouble whatsoever getting to sleep afterwards and I slipped through into our bedroom as soon as the first rumbles shook the bed."

"What did the doctor say?" I ask. "She told me that losing weight would help – I'm still working on that – and that cutting down on alcohol wouldn't be a bad idea either." Harry says. "She also suspected that I might have sleep apnea and referred me to a specialized sleep clinic for observations. They confirmed it, and now I have to wear a Continuous Positive Airflow Pressure (CPAP) mask to bed." I asked him to show me. It looked like something out of a war museum and I obviously didn't hide my reaction very well: "It's not as bad as it looks" he says, "and now I can sleep properly and don't feel zombified all day."

"Harry still snores loud enough to wake the neighbors, but without threatening to blow away our marriage" Liz says smiling. "We still stay in separate rooms and that may not work for some couples but I often stay with him until he falls asleep; our sex-life has never been better and Harry is so much more relaxed. My only advice to others would be to seek help and remember that when it comes to your partner snoring, you don't have the luxury of being able to suffer in silence."

Play it safe:

Although a great sex-life will bring you closer to your partner and boost your overall personal wellbeing, precautions must still be taken, regardless of age. It is easy to assume that just because pregnancy is no longer an issue, safe-sex practices become less significant in later-life too: this is absolutely not the case.

Although experts are unclear about whether it is due to the ubiquity of impotency drugs, the spike in divorce rates among older people, general ignorance surrounding safe-sex practices, or all of the above, one thing is certain: Sexually Transmitted Diseases (STDs) are on the rise amongst older people.

Prophylactics such as condoms or femidoms are very effective in preventing the transmission of STDs and should always be used, particularly if you are single and have just got back into the dating game. If you are using lube, remember to ensure that it is 'latex-friendly'.

A 2008 study published in the informatively but ominously titled journal, *Sexually Transmitted Infections*, indicated that STD rates have more than doubled among people aged 45 or older in less than a decade. The study's author, Dr. Babatunde Olowokure, emphasizes that even this figure only takes into account those people who sought treatment and the extra social stigma placed on sex in later-life can make it particularly difficult for retirees to seek help.

Baby Boomers and beyond are ready and willing to talk about their emotions and share their feelings and fears regarding sex far more than society often assumes. The risk of asking an 'embarrassing' question is far out-weighed by the liberating affect of being able to talk openly about these common post-retirement experiences.

Erectile dysfunction treatments such as Viagra can work wonders, but it is important to remember that it is intimacy not intercourse that should be the focus. Viagra will only help you achieve an erection; it won't make you happier with your partner or resolve a personal neurosis where talking could be the only treatment that's called for. As Dr Steven Lamm points out in his seminal book on erectile dysfunction, The Hardness Factor "there are some who may have adjusted to life without sex. Perhaps the woman doesn't really want it anymore, for one reason or another. And for those couples, the introduction of an ED drug can throw them seriously out of sync."

The life-enhancing benefits that a varied sex-life confers on your physical and mental wellbeing must make you question as a couple and individually, whether this is just because you are out of the habit, and if you are, get back in the habit! As Jack and Edna Jones were testament to, it is vital to maintain your physical and mental health, the other two elements of 'the magic three' to enjoy a great sex-life after retirement.

+ Erectile dysfunction is very common and very treatable.

+ Viagra can work wonders but communication can be equally as effective.

+ Sex is a habit. Get back in the habit if you think you have lost it.

+ Laugh and lighten up! Whether you're trying out a new penis pump, experimenting with new partners or role-playing The Wizard of Oz - you'll have more fun!

- Seeking professional help is not a personal failure; psychosexual therapy or relationship counselling won't give you all the answers, but will let you reflect on the situation in a 'safe place' helping you to reach your own realizations.

CHAPTER 5

THE MAGIC THREE

THE magic three is the interdependent triad at the core of your personal well-being: your physical health, your mindset, and your sex-life. A Chicago University study found that those who had sex more often in later-life rated their health more highly. Although scientists still don't know whether participants in the study had sex more often because they were healthier, or whether they

"The part can never be well unless the whole is well." – *Plato*

were healthier because they had more sex, the evidence points to a mutually reinforcing link - and that's good enough for me.

A 2005 study of retirement on lifestyle choices in relation to changes in weight led by Dr Astrid CJ Nooyens showed that those retiring from active jobs tended to gain more weight than their unretired colleagues, while those retiring from 'sedentary' roles lost more weight. The study goes to show that you need to reevaluate your energy intake and exercise program when you retire.

"Be careful about reading health books. You may die of a misprint." – *Mark Twain*

Armed with this knowledge and a little conviction, you can add years to your life with only a few minor tweaks – almost like a dodgy car mechanic fiddling the speedometer.

While it is crucial to remain mindful of your personal well-being in retirement, obsessing over health food fads and assuming that every blemish is the beginning of the end is unhealthy and will only make you miserable.

It is normal to worry about going to see the doctor at any age. I don't think the sweets and stickers in the dental surgery should only be limited to children because it doesn't get any easier. Whenever I have an upcoming medical appointment the questions and self-doubt shift into overdrive: what if they find something? What if one of my freckles has turned on me and become malignant? However much you hate visiting your doctor, it is especially important to not delay in retirement in the unlikely event that it is something serious; remember that in the majority of cases, even serious things can be fixed.

When the doctor told me I had a thyroid deficiency my whole life flashed in front of me. But on reflection I realized that the medication I was taking meant that I could lose weight without trying; my concentration span seemed to increase, as did my energy levels – who knew there could be an upside to health problems?

To stay healthy in retirement it is important to be mindful of your health, remember that you are entitled to be happy, healthy, successful and loved, follow some simple common-sense principles and leave room for levity in your health and exercise program; as happiness guru, Professor Ed Diener says:

❝ Current health recommendations focus on four things: avoid obesity, eat right, don't smoke, and exercise. It may be time to add 'be happy and avoid chronic anger and depression' to the list." –
Professor Ed Diener

In 1979 social psychologist Ellen J. Langer carried out her now famous week-long 'Counter Clockwise' study, transporting a group of elderly people (with their permission) to an environment mocked-up to resemble a typical home 1959 - complete with newspapers, magazines and music from that era. The group was told to behave as they would have back in 1959 and the age-reversing results of the study were remarkable:

+ Grip strength, posture and range of movement increased significantly

+ 63 percent tested higher on intelligence tests

+ And – by far the best news of all - objective observers concluded that they all looked younger after the study.

The message here isn't to put down this book, backdate your furnishings and swap your TV for a gramophone. Just don't underestimate the impact of your mindset on the overall quality of your life. As with changing your surroundings to renew your sex-life, not only can you talk yourself into feeling younger, but altering your mindset will have discernable positive physiological effects.

We have established that the vast majority of sexual dysfunction cases in men are precipitated by physical problems and those who consider their health as 'poor' are less likely to be sexually active than those who perceive themselves to be in good health. But what does 'good health' even mean? The answer isn't as straightforward as you might think.

Our bodies are constantly in a state of flux and our psychology directly influences our physiology. Even a doctor taking your blood pressure or heart rate etc. is only doing so in that moment; the second after you leave the doctor's surgery could be the moment you develop a problem that would have been detected ten seconds previously (or get hit by a bus). But this isn't anything to be anxious about. Stay positive, follow the following common-sense principles and look left, right and then left again before crossing the road.

If at first you don't succeed quit and quit again...

Before all else, the most important thing you can do for your health in retirement is *STOP SMOKING!* I was a 20-a-day man for nearly 25 years and we all now know just how bad smoking is for our health – they even come with pictures for people too lazy to read the somber warnings in block capitals on the front of the pack: **SMOKING KILLS**.

The benefits of quitting are enormous at any age. As well as prolonging your life by reducing the risk of cancer and heart disease, the immediate benefits include breathing easier, sleeping better and feeling more energetic. And I know I said I didn't do financial advice, but here's a handy money-saving tip for you: **STOP SMOKING**. Cigarettes aren't just bad for your health; they ravage your bank balance too.

If that wasn't enough, quitting smoking is also one of the best things you can do for your sex-life! Not only does it reduce the risk of ED directly by improving your physical health, but it makes you feel healthier which has an equally profound effect on your personal wellbeing. You may relapse more than once (as I did) – this is a natural part of the quitting process. But with advances in treatments including patches, gum, electronic pens, free advice from organizations such as The Foundation for a Smokefree America and the NHS, compounded by most governments implementing blanket bans on smoking in public places, the support is there to help you kick the habit for good.

When it comes to the magic three, stopping smoking is number one on the list and has immediately results, but Baby Boomers can be a resilient bunch with excuses flying thick and fast, the top two being:

Excuse 1:

"I'm too old, what's the point?" This is a terrible excuse. Research has shown that, regardless of your age, quitting smoking reduces the excess risk of having a heart attack by half.

Excuse 2:

(The wildly-exaggerated anecdote): "Rubbish! My next-door neighbor smoked until he was 95 and could still run a mile in under six minutes." Don't base your life-decisions on one-offs or unsubstantiated rumors – even if you haven't developed emphysema or another terrible smoking-related disease, that's not to say you won't – it's always worth quitting.

Booze: The bane of a healthy retirement

If you are reading these diet-tips while swigging a bottle of whiskey then stop for a moment. Most guidelines recommended drinking no more than 21 units for a man per week (and no more than 4 units in one sitting) and for the ladies, no more than 14 units per week and no more than 3 units in one sitting. Just to jog your memory (in case it's been ravaged by booze) a unit is roughly equivalent to half a pint of normal strength lager, a small glass of wine, or a 25cl shot of spirits.

The stress that comes with retirement, whether job bereavement, through losing the sense of belonging to a community and not replacing this loss satisfactorily can lead to the bottle. This is a problem that too often goes unnoticed as retirees frequently hide their addiction by drinking at home. Heavy drinking is disastrous for your health not to mention your sex-life. If a woman drinks far too much she will become temporarily anorgasmic, but if the man has drunk too much then this won't be much of an issue anyway.

The delights of dieting

There is always a diet revolution capturing the public imagination; a celebrity or medical-maverick endorsed program that promises to help you lose more weight, faster, with less effort – from only eating foods of a certain colour, at a certain time of day etc.

Dieting isn't easy. If losing weight was as simple as piling it on, the term 'super-morbidly obese' might never have been coined, and the phrase 'we're going to need the winch for this one' wouldn't be the second-most common phrase used by firemen after: 'someone get the ladder, that cat just isn't coming down...'.

Some diets are backed by solid research and provide you with the nutrients and energy needed to stay healthy in retirement, but others can be downright dangerous.

Crash diets are like an odd reversion of the 'stone soup' story that I used to read my children. For those of you who were never read bedtime stories (or never read to your kids) it's about a couple of travellers who visit a nearby town and claim that they can make a delicious soup with just a pan of water and a stone. The villagers are understandably sceptical, but hungry, so oblige. "Now all we need are some potatoes" they say, so the villagers bring a sack of potatoes. "Now all we need are some leeks" they say - so the villagers bring armfuls of leeks, and so on until they have all the ingredients for a delicious soup. The chefs take out the magic stone – and voila! Stone soup, made with nothing but a stone, a pan of water, and all the villagers' vegetables.

Any diet that revolves around the principle of 'eat very little of the same low calorie, bland food for breakfast and lunch and that eat whatever you want for dinner!' is so blatantly ridiculous that you'd think that people would laugh it off - but they don't, because of all the buzz created by testimonials such as: "I lost 40 pounds on the cereal/cabbage soup... diet – it really works!" complete with obviously doctored photographs. That and we're all desperate for that ever-elusive easy-fix. Of course you can eat very little of something healthy for two meals, build up a calorie deficit (remain ravenously hungry and dangerously irritable throughout the day) and then eat a large dinner and lose weight.

REMEMBER: Don't starve yourself, not least because not eating isn't the quickest way to lose weight as it slows your metabolism, causing you to burn calories at a slower rate than a well-regulated eating and exercise program. You need to choose the foods that will make you feel most full whilst giving you the nutrients you need.

Use common sense and don't cling on to fads that promise you miracle results for minimal effort. You will slip into a cycle of hope and despair that will only make you want to eat even more. A couple of recent examples include:

The Blood group diet

+ The Blood group diet advocates eating specific foods based on your ancestral blood group i.e. 'O' is the hunter blood type and the advice for this group is to consume a higher protein diet. The diet was created by the very successful Dr Peter D'Adamo, a naturopathic doctor. Never heard of a naturopathic? Neither had I. I am not impressed with this diet!

Baby food diet

+ It is sometimes said that old age is the beginning of your second childhood so it makes sense to go back to eating baby food, right? Endorsed by A-list celebrity, Jennifer Aniston, this diet is as disgusting as it sounds. Each meal consists of either a jar of baby food, or assorted pureed fruit and vegetables. The baby food diet carries the unsurprising advantage that modest portion sizes are already taken care of (because the jars are intended for babies), and it will tend to be low in fat, rich in vitamins and minerals and free from any nasty additives.

Wonder drugs

Remember Roald Dahl's classic, Charlie and the Chocolate Factory where Willy Wonka invents a magic meal replacement gum? People are obsessed with the idea of the 'holy grail' solution to all of life's problems. Unfortunately, as you will remember, Willy Wonka's creation hasn't been perfected as the aptly named Violet discovers when she starts chewing it and turns into a giant blueberry. Even Willy Wonka couldn't have devised something as disgusting as diet pills.

By far the most popular, and the first over-the-counter drug of its kind, is alli which lowers the amount of fat your body absorbs by 25%. alli's weight-reducing properties have been scientifically verified, but the drug has become more synonymous with its side-effects...

The pill is marketed as part of a wider healthy eating plan, but if you don't stick to the diet and eat too much fat, be prepared for such pleasantries as wind, diarrhea, incontinence and sometimes all three at once. My view is: why run the risk of soiling yourself in public when you could be losing weight by eating healthily anyway and saving money too?

Desperate times, desperate measures

We all get desperate sometimes. I've tried the bread and butter diet and the cabbage soup diet. I also jumped on the Atkins bandwagon, which cuts out carbohydrates, meaning no bread, pasta, cereal and other staple foods. The diet works fantastically well so long as you don't start sneaking carbs back in to your meals while continuing to eat exactly the same amount of fat, as I discovered in my own independent study involving just me and piles of bread.

I first joined Slimming World but was asked to leave after three weeks because I wasn't taking it seriously enough. When the class leader asked: "When you open the fridge and see a big bottle of mayonnaise what do you do?" I shouted out "take a huge dollop". It turned out we differed on our idea of what counts as 'amusing' and I was shown the door. I like to think I was a dieting martyr. Fortunately she changed her mind and I was invited back the following week. One week I lost the most weight in the class and won some hairspray. I think it might have been the instructor's way of getting back at me, giving the guy who's thinning on top the hair products.

I remember joining Weight-Watchers and after weighing myself in front of the room the instructor saying, "Well done Larry you've lost 1 and 1/2 pounds!" While I was thinking, one and a half bloody pounds, after starving myself for 3 weeks.

It can be difficult joining slimming groups where you have to weigh yourself in public but you need to get over your scale-phobia: ignorance is the dieter's road to ruin. The class was made up of 95% women but the sense of community in the group was very helpful and I would recommend it to those looking to have fun and lose weight at the same time.

By far my worst dieting experience was a session of hypnotherapy that still lingers in my memory. I'm not saying that all hypnotherapy is terrible, in fact it did help me to overcome anxiety following a family bereavement, but as far as weight-loss treatments go, it wasn't my cup of tea...

I can make you sick: the horror of hypnotherapy

These hypnotherapists are something else. At the first session mine asked me to close my eyes and imagine myself in a mirrored room, and then he asked me to imagine myself undressed.

"How do you look?" he asked.

"Big," I replied.

"Now, imagine a big table in the middle of the room, crammed with your favourite foods." I could see thick juicy steaks, pizza, chips on one half and a selection of desserts on the other: lemon meringue, sticky toffee pudding, crème brulee; you name it - I was salivating at the thought of it, all perfectly prepared and glistening with fat.

"Now go to the table and start eating Larry, it's ok, go on..."

After an imaginary wedge of chocolate cake topped with a small shovel of ice cream I was beginning to enjoy hypnotherapy.

"What can you see now Larry?"

"A trifle."

"Cut a nice big piece, treat yourself." I obliged.

"What do you look like now Larry?"

"Fatter," I whispered, feeling increasingly sick.

"Have another slice of cake," he said. "Tastes good doesn't it? Now what do you look like?"

"Huge," I rasped.

After an hour of this cruelty I felt incredibly nauseas, but thankfully, the experience was coming to an end. I could hear the hypnotherapist's voice from afar, beckoning me back into the room.

"Ok Larry, when you wake up you will no longer feel the need to binge-eat. You will eat moderately, and you will remember that feeling of sickness whenever you feel the urge to binge: 10, 9, 8, 7, 6, 5, 4, 3, 2, 1 – now open your eyes Larry."

"Thank you, thank you, doctor," I muttered, already halfway out the door. "See you next week." I never went back.

The urge to retch had almost passed and the sick feeling in the pit of my stomach had been replaced with a more familiar one: ravenous hunger. All that talking about food had worked up quite an appetite – luckily there was a McDonald's next door –a Big Mac with super size fries was exactly what I needed after that ordeal.

So what actually works?

Although there is no one miracle plan that will solve all your problems, different people find certain diets easier to stick to in the long-run and that there are certain foods which can help - it is a case of finding out what works for you and making sure that you consider your health holistically instead of obsessing over weight-loss.

Healthy eating will improve your physical health by reducing the risk of heart attack, stroke and Type 2 diabetes. Eating a healthy and balanced diet rich in the right vitamins, minerals and nutrients is a vital aspect of 'the magic three' and will boost your personal well-being in retirement. Enjoy the experience of eating, the sensuality of food and avoid falling into the vicious circle of unsustainable deprivation, binging and guilt.

A study published in 2009 by the New England Journal of Medicine assigned different diets to 811 overweight or obese people focusing on different ratios of fat, protein and carbs. In addition, each participant was asked to cut 750 calories from their average daily food intake and the results revealed that the diet-type didn't significantly affect the amount of weight lost.

The Mediterranean Diet has grown in popularity and researchers have conducted long-term studies to determine its effects on health, particularly looking at life expectancy. In a ten-year study from 1995 to 2005 involving more than 200,000 men and 166,000 women, researchers assessed how closely participants followed the Mediterranean diet according to a nine point system and then studied the relationship between the Mediterranean Diet, health and longevity.

The results showed that those sticking to the diet were around 12 to 20% less likely to die of 'all causes', including cancer and heart disease, and the more you stuck to the diet, the more healthy years of life expectancy you could expect to enjoy.

A 2010 study of 2,148 people of retirement age led by Dr Yian Gu at Columbia University, New York, also revealed that a healthier diet greatly lessened the chances of developing Alzheimer's disease.

The participants were all aged 65 or over and did not have Alzheimer's at the start of the study. They supplied detailed dietary information and were then tested for the disease every eighteen months. People eating a higher proportion of salad dressing, nuts, fish, poultry, fruits and green leafy vegetables – foods often associated with the 'Mediterranean diet' – were far less likely to develop the alzheimer's when compared to those with a penchant for high-fat dairy, red meat and butter.

The science bit

I'm not saying that the Mediterranean Diet is the only way to go, but it shows that eating a sensible, healthy diet low in saturated fats is greatly beneficial to your health, particularly in retirement. If you want to stay healthy then listen to the science rather than the fads:

Eat more fibre to aid digestion. Wholegrain cereal, porridge, wholegrain bread, brown pasta and brown rice, pulses such as beans or lentils, fresh fruit and vegetables can help allay the bowel problems that can develop with aging.

Take calcium and vitamin D for strong bones to protect against osteoporosis in later-life - sunlight is a great source of Vitamin D – you don't even have to do anything except stand outside!

Eat more low-fat dairy it decreases the absorption of fat by your gut meaning that you could eat the same amount as before and lose weight. Forget diet pills, stick to low-fat dairy and you'll also get the calcium you need too; try switching fruit juices for milk (but remember to eat your five fruit and vegetables a day).

Remember that 'low-fat' may sound like something your cardiologist would approve of, but it is too often marketing spin for 'high salt' which is just as bad, if not worse. Always check nutritional information on food packaging, or buy the sort of food that doesn't come with nutritional information stickers on it, like fruit and vegetables.

Folate (found in brown rice, cereals, fruit and vegetables) and vitamin B12 (shellfish, meat, cheese and commonly taken in supplement form) have been found to improve memory and mental performance in women over 65 years of age in a study by the Center for Scientific and Industrial Research Organisation on women aged 20-92.

Omega 3 fatty acid is found in fish. A Dutch study found that elderly men who ate a lot of fish were least likely to develop dementia.

The joy of food

If you're still not convinced, the other advantage of eating healthily in retirement is the amazing affect that it can have on your sex-life - I'm talking apples as well as aphrodisiacs. In retirement there are a few food rules to bear in mind when it comes to getting frisky. As a general rule: if it's good for your heart then it's great for your sex-life because sexual functioning depends so much on your circulation:

Relish the sensuality of food. Feed your partner chocolate-covered strawberries in the bath, but make sure you are familiar with the Heimlich manoeuvre just in case, and don't clog the plughole.

While we're on the subject of chocolate – eat more of it. Yes, that's right. A study published in the Journal of Sexual Medicine showed that eating one square of dark chocolate a day can boost your sex-life. The cocoa in chocolate contains phenylethylamine, also known as the 'love-chemical' – the same chemical released by the brain at the point of orgasm.

Avoid 'heavy' foods like a chicken masala with onion pilau, a garlic and coriander naan bread and mango lassie – it might sound nice, but all that heavy food will make you bloated, sluggish and definitely not in the mood for love.

Is that a zucchini in your pocket or are you just pleased to see me?

Although there is no scientific proof to support the effectiveness of aphrodisiacs (named after 'Aphrodite' the Greek goddess of love and beauty), there is no denying that the sexually suggestive shapes, tantalizing texture and general jouissance of certain foods can make a real difference in the bedroom, as well as livening up your culinary creations.

Foods such as oysters, lobster tails, saffron and champagne all have something else in common: they're bloody expensive. At least part of the aphrodisiac effect is your partner knowing that you've gone all out to impress them. If you're known as the perennial tight-wad then a saffron and crab-infused soufflé will definitely surprise your partner and revitalise your sex-life in retirement.

To maintain your personal well-being you need to maintain your energy balance while making sure that you also take in all of the nutrition that you need through the calories that you are ingesting. But diet is only one side of the story; the other is exercise.

Your exercise epiphany

The tension between our body image and the way we are perceived by others is something which most of us constantly wrestle with. These perspectives can be thought of as occupying opposite ends of a seesaw; minor wobbles go unnoticed until we hit a tipping point, reflect on our lifestyle and redress the balance: this is your exercise epiphany.

It may happen as you're walking along, see a chunky guy tucking into a pretzel and think "some people never learn" before realizing that it isn't just some chunky guy, it's you. The inevitable lifestyle changes that accompany retirement, from eating at irregular intervals as you learn to adapt to the absence of full-time work, not getting as much exercise or failing to notice the gradual increase in alcohol consumption as Friday night drinks turn into Tuesday morning eye-openers, means that this is a time where you are particularly susceptible to unhealthy fluctuations in weight and other health issues.

It could be trying on some old jeans and telling yourself that sure they may not be the loosest fit in the world, but as long as you don't need to bend down, eat, or take them off again, you'll be fine.

My personal tipping point came during a vacation to celebrate Michele's birthday. I decided to surprise her with a long weekend in Barcelona and after several hours of getting lost down several dodgy-looking side-streets, my ankles throbbed and I looked like I'd run a marathon while Michele remained immaculate as usual. It struck me that I wasn't the fit Larry of old: urgent action was required.

You may agonize over which slice of cheese-cake or large glass of red was responsible for catapulting you through the weight-divisions. As we all know it wasn't one burger, one tub of ice-cream or even one of the multipacks of Jaffa cakes that I scoffed on my own while no one was looking, it comes down to simple lifestyle choices and your approach to the magic three.

Even if you feel yourself slipping into bad habits in retirement, it is never too late to work yourself out of them. Remember Aesop's fable, The Tortoise and the Hare? The moral of the story is: slow and steady wins the race. It's a nice story, but I'm not buying it. Retirement in the 21st Century means that we can stay happy, fit and sexually active for longer than ever before and that doesn't mean living life in the slow-lane.

CHAPTER 6

FROM TORTOISE TO HARE

MODERN theories of aging suggest that rather than our physical health tapering off with age we can look forward to staying healthier for longer, and eventually drop off after a long, fast and fulfilling life. Whether you choose to take this opportunity is a totally different matter and a decision that ultimately rests with you. As the old joke goes:

QUESTION: How many psychiatrists does it take to change a light bulb?

ANSWER: One, but the light bulb has got to want to change.

This terrible joke epitomised my attitude to exercise throughout a fairly sizeable chunk of my life where I was myself, a fairly sizeable chunk. I knew the benefits of a healthy-lifestyle deep down, but thinking about my fitness (or lack thereof) felt like opening Pandora's Box; I preferred to live in blissful ignorance.

REMEMBER: If you've been out of the game for a long time then always consult a health professional before starting any exercise program.

Research at Duke University in North Carolina suggests that the most common reason for our sex-life dwindling in later life is a decline in physical health and the pain or discomfort caused by common ailments such as heart disease, weak tendons and painful joints. Exercise can prevent these problems from emerging and dramatically improve your standard of living and sex-life throughout your 70s, 80s and beyond!

And don't worry, just because exercise is good for you doesn't mean that it has to be boring, costly, or hard work. As well as improving your physical health in retirement, living a more active lifestyle will help you to:

+ Look and feel great

+ Socialize and meet new people

+ Prepare for a more rounded and energetic sex-life

Despite these benefits, people of all ages have an incredible ability to generate half-baked excuses to get out of exercising (usually grounded in myth or laziness) such as: "I have never exercised properly so there's no point in starting now!" Rubbish. A study published in the Archives of Internal Medicine in 2008 found that men who regularly exercised, even after the age of 70 were 30% less likely to die before the age of 90 – don't lose heart – start exercising today.

Other classics include:

+ I don't have time

It's more likely that you're just being lazy. Make time.

+ I hate going to the gym

A lot of people hate going to the gym, and with its mirrored walls, posers, machines coated in a film of other people's sweat, cheesy dance music that you can't help moving in time to as if trapped in some tacky TV-ad for a dirty phone-line, it isn't too hard to see why. But the gym can be a great place to meet new people.

I don't have enough money

Exercise doesn't have to be expensive. Gym memberships may seem steep but exercising at home or outside is free: view it as an investment in your future happiness. How often to you go out to a restaurant? Cut out one of these nights and you would probably save enough money for a session with a personal trainer.

My health is too poor

While it is true that disability can impede certain exercises or activities, 99.9% of people are capable of at least some form of exercise however light. You can do mild therapeutic exercises and specialized stretching to strengthen the muscles; exercise can give you an endorphin rush and make you feel great.

Instead of looking for excuses NOT to exercise, look for excuses to exercise

Try to find ways to make lasting changes to your lifestyle. Here are a few ideas to get you started:

Get a dog, think of it as an obesity indicator: if your dog gets fat, you're not getting enough exercise; if the dog dies of congestive heart failure you should see a doctor as soon as possible (but don't run and try to avoid loud noises).

The old classic: get off the bus a couple of stops earlier than usual and walk the rest of the way; better yet, invite your retired friends around and burn your bus passes then walk the whole way.

You know those slim athletic people you see bounding up the stairs at train stations while you're eating a sausage roll on the escalator? They're slim and athletic for a reason. Seemingly insignificant lifestyle choices like taking the stairs soon add up. Forcing yourself to break unhealthy habits and adopting a healthier mindset is the way to change your life, not crash diets or extreme exercise programs.

Physical inactivity is no laughing matter and, according to the World Health Organisation, it is one of the main causes of death across the developed work causing heart disease, cancer, diabetes and strokes.

Weighing up the relative merits of every single exercise is a favourite tactic of the seasoned procrastinator. The time you spend thinking about what to do could be spent doing instead. That said, endurance, strength, flexibility and balance should all be taken into account – many exercises crossover these areas - and the 'community' aspect of exercising can enhance your enjoyment, increasing the likelihood of sticking with it.

Remember that one person's 'low intensity' exercise is another person's herculean challenge. Start at a level at which you feel comfortable and work your way to improved fitness at your own pace – starting is half the battle.

The relative intensity of exercises is often measured in MET (Metabolic Equivalent). This refers to the metabolic rate (i.e. the rate at which your body uses energy in a given period). One MET is defined as burning 1 kcal (calorie) per kg of your body weight per hour and is the amount of energy expended at rest – i.e. the normal speed of your metabolism. With this in mind, here is a brief guide to the relative intensity of different exercises:

Low intensity (< 3)	Moderate intensity (3 to 6)	High intensity (> 6)
Watching TV	Walking	Rope jumping
Sewing	Fishing	Squash
Gardening	Dancing	Aerobics
Light walking	Golfing	Climbing
Archery	Mowing the lawn	Martial Arts

MYTH: Having sex is the equivalent of a three-mile run

FACT: If you can't run three miles then it isn't.

Sorry to break it to you, but research has shown that contrary to popular opinion, sex with a long-term partner is equivalent to "walking a mile in approximately 20 minutes on level ground" (3-4 METs), classed as low to moderate intensity exercise, with heart-rate and blood pressure peaking at the point of orgasm, although your total energy expenditure will vary according to:

+ Your current level of fitness

+ Your partner's level of fitness

+ The position(s) you try. Sex with the man on top involves higher energy expenditure for both partners than the other way around (although calorie estimates widely vary).

Regardless of the gymnastics involved or vigorousness of your encounters, sex is fantastic aerobic exercise and it can even be enjoyable sometimes too! A groundbreaking 1997 study of 1,222 people from Caerphilly in South Wales found that men who had fewer orgasms were twice as likely to die as those who had two or more orgasms a week and that having sex three or more times a week halved the risk of heart attack or stroke.

Fast-forward more than a decade and much is now being made of a 2011 study linking sex and exercise in later-life to an increased risk of heart attack in inactive people. As you would expect of any study looking at both sex and death, the press had a field day trying to churn out the most pessimistic headlines possible, despite one of the study's authors, Dr Issa Dahabreh, stating that "one should not interpret our findings as meaning that physical activity or sexual activity are dangerous or harmful."

MYTH: Sex in later-life could lead to a heart-attack.

FACT: It's not impossible but the idea of a heart attack in the throes of passion might make compelling TV, but the chances of it happening in real-life are approximately 3 in a million – roughly equivalent to the chances of choking to death on your next meal. So if you're going to give up sex on medical grounds, you should probably stop eating as well, and crossing roads, or going outside at all...

Doctors recommend that we should take 30 minutes of breathless exercise five times a week (a total of 150 minutes) but only 30% of people aged from 50-64 meet this recommendation according to saga.co.uk.

If 30 minute chunks sound a little bit too much like hard work then have no fear, splitting your exercise sessions into ten-minute blasts is just as effective, as a study by Loughborough University showed.

Use your brain:

I hope the estate of former US president John Quincy Adams won't mind me surmising his eloquent words in slightly simpler terms: use it or lose it! As you exercise more, increase your fitness and notice that paunch starting to retreat, you are more likely to pay attention to other aspects of your health; increasing your chance of quitting smoking and cutting down on the booze. Adopting a proactive attitude toward exercise will help reverse and allay any negative effects on your physical and mental health and ensure that you have a great sex-life in retirement.

> **❝ Old minds are like old horses; you must exercise them if you wish to keep them in working order."** –
> *John Quincy Adams*

I'm no brain surgeon as you know, but the idea that we are somehow powerless to stop the degeneration of our brain as we age is a myth created by younger people who are guilty of speaking before engaging their brains. A 2006 study published in the Journal of Gerontology and led by Stanley J. Colcombe found that, not only could aerobic exercise slow down the effects of aging on the volume of the brain, (a physical measure associated with a higher IQ), but it could actually reverse them. Furthermore, the study suggested that only a 'minimal' amount of effort was required to minimize loss of brain volume in later-life.

The brain is constantly developing throughout our life, forming new neural pathways like the roots of a tree that continue to sprawl and intersect as we interact with the world around us. These branches are called 'dendrites' – from the Greek word 'dendron' meaning 'tree' (Greek lesson over). Dendrites need to be activated in order to unlock your true potential. Just as you don't want your body getting stiff, achy and unresponsive, you need to consciously work your brain to keep it limber.

Research has shown that brain training games aimed at families and number games like Sudoku only improve how good you are at the particular game you're playing: if the game is to remember how many sheep jump over a virtual gate for example, you may become better at counting sheep jumping over a gate, but this will be of no other benefit in your life - unless you're a shepherd.

Side-stepping stress and ducking depression

Stress is often mistakenly viewed as an exclusively mental affliction, but it can have far-reaching implications on your physical health and on your sex-life. Just some of the physical symptoms include headaches, indigestion, irritable bowel syndrome, muscle pain, insomnia and erectile dysfunction.

Low-impact exercises like tai-chi, Pilates and yoga can help ward off stress and lower the risk of depression. The isolation, loss of status and social interaction accompanying retirement can bring on symptoms of stress and depression. Exercise will make you feel better about yourself and enhance every aspect of your personal well-being. A study in 1999 led by Dr James Blumenthal at Duke University Medical Center compared the effects of exercise and anti-depressants on a group of 156 people aged 50+, and found that exercise was an effective treatment for depression only if the participants were motivated enough to exercise.

We know that aerobic activity such as brisk walking, light rowing, cycling, swimming etc., increases the flow of oxygen-rich blood to the brain, improving mental health but research by the University of British Columbia found that resistance training using free weights, weight machines and squats/lunges significantly improved results on memory, decision-making and conflict resolution tests by 12.6% - so you can battle the bulge and flay the flab while give your brain a boost too!

REMEMBER: Regardless of how often you exercise or which specific activities you choose to involve yourself make sure you enjoy what you are doing otherwise you will be far more likely to quit. Exercising less often or less intensely than you 'should' is far better for you than doing nothing at all.

A proactive mindset is the path to a proactive life

The benefits of exercise on your mental health are not merely confined to stress and depression, but extend to keeping dementia at bay as well. A study based in Germany recorded the health and exercise levels of 3,486 elderly people without dementia. After two years the scientists reevaluated the participants, compared the two sets of data and concluded that those who exercise a minimum of three times a week were half as likely to develop dementia in later-life.

The 'protective effect' of exercise against dementia was not dependent on the intensity of the exercise, or how late you leave it. Lead author of the study, professor of psychiatry and psychotherapy Dr Thorleif Etgen from Munchen University said: "even if you start late in life, at 60 or 70, there is a benefit, for it's never too late to start exercising."

Maslow's hierarchy of needs (the groovy pyramid from Chapter one) classifies health and well-being as a 'safety need', the satiety of which is a fundamental step to happiness in retirement. Exercise not only contributes toward good mental and physical health but also constitutes gainfully spent leisure time, giving you a sense of purpose and social interaction: a proactive attitude is the start to a proactive attitude to life.

A journey of a thousand miles...

Richard, a recently retired dentist, and Shirley, a deputy head mistress of a school on the outskirts of Manchester, lived in a domestic paradise consisting of two old Labradors, a large fireplace in the living room with an old-fashioned copper ash bucket on the hearth, an AGA in the kitchen finished off with the 'Welcome Home' mat at the front door. It felt like someone had given the builders a Beatrix Potter story as a blueprint.

I met this couple through a local ramblers' association. I didn't really push the sex angle at that point, thinking that ramblers aren't generally known for their sexploits, but I knew the couple enjoyed walking and that seemed like a fitting starting-point.

"I was looking on the internet for a week-long vacation somewhere and saw walking trips advertised at a health spa less than an hour's drive away." Shirley says. "It wasn't cheap but the idea of just getting away and having a detox sounded perfect. I wanted to lose some weight and they really pamper you at those places."

I ask her how it all worked and what she enjoyed the most about the trip.

"We were split into small groups first of all and asked to walk around a field in the way we would normally walk. I didn't even know that there was such a thing as 'normal walking' at that time, but the instructor emphasized the importance of your posture because of the impact that it has on your balance, strengthening and toning your core muscles. It sounds serious but it was a lot of fun really."

"It was around that time the 10,000 step program became so popular" Richard says. "I don't know how they came up with the number but the idea is that you get a pedometer and try to walk 10,000 steps everyday –the optimal amount of exercise to maintain good health and weight control."

"As usual, Richard was the best in the class" Shirley says. "He finished the exercise first (even though the instructor repeatedly said that it wasn't a race) and praised his technique. I lagged behind with the other stragglers. It was a giggle, but I felt like I had learned something and it was a nice way to spend a week in the country – the food was incredible too; healthy and delicious."

"I have to admit, one can get bored walking around the block around here for the millionth time" Richard says, "but I bought myself an iPod and listen to music whenever I go out. I would say that you should watch where you're going if you decide to do that, it can be hazardous crossing roads."

I wanted to find out if this extended to their sex-life and was glad that they were willing to briefly broach the subject.

"We did go through a difficult patch" Shirley says. "Richard has always worked so hard, and I appreciate everything he has done for the family, as well as helping us to set up this beautiful home - but I won't deny that it was frustrating when we had planned a romantic night in, I spend all afternoon making dinner and he wouldn't get back home until 8 or 9 o'clock that night - retirement meant that he didn't have any more excuses!"

"I know it's become somewhat fashionable to see retirement as a great new beginning" Richard says "but with the kids away from the house, we're not as guarded and our sex-life is a lot more spontaneous."

Richard tells me that he still edits articles for a medical journal and is occasionally contacted by ex-colleagues seeking advice, but doesn't miss the 12-hour days and has replaced the structure of the workplace in his leisure time.

"It's easy to lose sight of what you're working for" Richard says. "We've had a wonderful family, sent them to a good school and got this house exactly how we wanted it. It's time for us to enjoy ourselves and – I can't speak for Shirley, but I feel like we have renewed our relationship."

"He's a big softie really" Shirley says.

Run for your life!

Once you're comfortable with walking and your shiny new pedometer tells you that you are regularly exceeding the recommended number of steps for maintaining a healthy weight and boosting your overall health (a 2008 study actually showed that this was 8,000 for women over-60 and 11,000 for men of the same age) you might want to consider stepping it up a notch and start running...

Researchers from Stanford University School of Medicine showed that running can slow the aging process and elderly joggers were half as likely die prematurely from serious conditions like cancer than non-runners.

In 2008 Dr James Fries monitored a group of 500 runners and a group of non-runners for more than 20 years. After 19 years, 34% of the non-runners had died compared with only 15% of the runners. Although both groups had become more disabled with age, running seemed to delay the onset of disability by an average of 16 years. Not only that, but as the years progressed, the gap in health between the runners and non-runners widened considerably.

REMEMBER: No matter how much you try and persuade yourself otherwise there will always be some exercises that you loathe: the secret is to stick with the ones that you hate the least. Don't set yourself an unrealistically rigid program. Go easy on yourself and make sure you're enjoying what you're doing otherwise you're not only likely to quit, but the stress of keeping up your regime will be detrimental to your health.

Whatever you choose to do, set targets and chart your progress. Don't use a romanticized 21-year-old version of yourself as a benchmark either. Set yourself realistic goals and don't be too hard on yourself if you don't meet them. There is a steep learning curve associated with tending to your personal wellbeing; if this weren't true the world would be a much healthier place.

Golf, and why there definitely is a God*

In my twenties I worked as an export manager for a large American manufacturing company specializing in various products including top-of-the-line golf clubs. I was 'invited' to attend a compulsory golf tournament in my home town and would be forced to showcase my malcoordination in front of my co-workers.

As I trudged to the first hole I heard a wonderful sound; an ominous rumble and the dark clouds in the distance rolled in; moments later people were shaking their heads and looking up at the sky, a sheet of lightening turned the grey a pale yellow and a downpour of biblical proportions flooded the course. I don't know if it was divine intervention but I can honestly say that I've never been so happy to be standing in the middle of a storm in my life. The tournament was duly cancelled and my dignity spared! Amen.

An activity that I find far more fun, and like to think I'm considerably better at, is one where you don't need to traipse around a field for hours on end, you don't have to embarrass yourself in front of your coworkers (although some people do) and the object is to let the other person win: that's right, I'm talking about sex. And it's not just great exercise but it could actually save your life too...

* If you type Larry Gould into Google one of the top hits is a blog by a different Larry Gould who has a passion for golf. I would like to clarify that: 1. This is not me; and 2. I don't make a habit of Googling myself (or 'egosurfing' as it has been dubbed), honestly.

Body image

If after reading the last few pages you are wringing your hands in despair thinking that you didn't want to have to actually do anything except get rid of those wrinkles and shift a couple of pounds then I feel your pain – looking good is often a key motivator for exercising, and it's as good as any other.

> **In our appearance-centric society, beauty is a huge factor in everyone's professional and emotional success – for good or ill, it's the way things are; accept it or go live under a rock."** –
>
> *Joan Rivers*

We are told not to judge a book by its cover, but we're a superficial bunch and form lasting (sometimes damning) impressions of people before they have even opened their mouths. Research shows that appearance impacts on every area of your life from getting off more lightly in court, to earning a higher salary. Whichever way you look at it: it pays to be beautiful.

Researchers from the University of Florida surveyed 200 men and women aged between 25 and 75, giving each person IQ and other intelligence tests and showed their pictures to another group to rate their attractiveness. The results showed that those considered 'good-looking' were paid more on average. Good-looking people tend to judge themselves more favorably, reinforcing their self-confidence and giving them an edge.

Look great, feel greater!

Internet search engine behemoth, Google has created a tool where you can enter two search terms to view the correlation between them. Bruce Upbin from Forbes.com found that there was a strong link between 'retirement' and 'plastic surgery', and there is little wonder, with people living longer and more active lives than ever.

Looking good isn't just a narcissistic preoccupation, or a competition - unless you're entering a beauty pageant. Feeling good about the way we look has two distinct benefits:

1. The way you look directly impacts on the way you feel. Looking your best boosts your self-confidence, radiating into your everyday life and opening you up to new ideas, experiences and people.

2. The way you look changes how other people treat you. If your dentist greets you with a toothless smile or your dermatologist has a Maori tattoo sprawled across one side of his face, then you'd probably run a mile; this isn't beauty bias, but the remnants of an evolved defense mechanism: scary-looking people could be dangerous, danger equals possible death, and we like to avoid death wherever possible.

Our celebrity-culture and the proliferation of air-brushed photography have created an unrealistic model of what we should like as we age. Not only do celebrities seem able to resist the inexorable tide of aging, but they now appear to have reversed it completely, just to rub our crinkled, imperfect faces in it. In a slightly perverse way, I guess we do have celebrities to thank for offering themselves up as human guinea pigs to cosmetic surgeons, showing Joe Average what works and what doesn't.

It isn't just women that are going under the knife; more men are getting plastic surgery by ever before. The American Society of Plastic Surgeons (ASPS) found that ever more men are opting for cosmetic surgery with 14 percent more facelifts and 7 percent more liposuction procedures in 2010 than the previous year.

If you are satisfied with your appearance then great. But if you aren't, don't feel pressured by the puritans who spout that cosmetic surgery is some kind of personal failing; an unnatural augmentation of your body which is somehow 'cheating' the aging process.

Your decision should be based on the following criteria alone:

+ Are you making the decision for you?

+ Have you researched and understood the health risks involved with surgery?

+ Do you have the money?

+ And **the million-dollar question:** Would you be happier knowing that you decided against surgery, kept the crow's feet that have been niggling you for so long but stayed 100% natural; or will you live by the more hedonistic mantra: "screw it, you only live once." I decided on the second option when I started losing my hair.

Hair today, gone tomorrow

I was always concerned about my receding hairline and chatted to a friend of mine who mysteriously developed a lustrous head of hair after going bald in his mid-twenties. He recommended booking a consultation with his Trichologist and I tentatively agreed. The original hair transplants were doll-like and unconvincing. You could see the holes where the hair had been plugged which not only drew attention to your thinning barnet but also told people that you were in denial as well.

For 12 hours I sat in the doctor's chair, doped up on valium watching Singing in the Rain and lapsing in and out of consciousness. The surgeon removed a strip of my scalp from the back of my head where the hair was thickest; it felt like he was tearing off a plaster as I tried to persuade the nurse for more valium.

The doctors removed the hair follicles from this strip and made thousands of painless micro-incisions on the top of my scalp. Over the next 10 hours they planted 3600 follicles where the hair was sparsest before sewing up the flap of skin – I felt like a human allotment. Now all I could do was wait and hope something would sprout.

1 month	nothing but redness and pain
3 months	patchy stubble
5 months	wispy baby-like hair, paranoid that I was destined for baldness
7 months	definite growth, perhaps it wasn't a waste of time and money after all…
9 months	…. FINALLY! Spring had sprung and for the first time in over a decade I needed a hairbrush.

The procedure lifted my confidence, and there is nothing more special than when my wife runs her fingers through my hair. I immediately felt 10 years younger and when I look at old photos of myself my only regret is not having the surgery earlier. The amazing thing is that, because the hair at the back of the head is genetically resistant to balding, the procedure can last a lifetime.

The desire to modify your appearance might be triggered by the breakdown of a relationship in retirement. Being in a long-term relationship gives you the time to build trust and break down insecurities regarding your appearance or parts of your body that you are particularly paranoid about. If you suddenly find yourself single again you can feel acutely self-conscious and undesirable; as one of the plastic surgeons that I spoke to told me with a porcelain smile on his face: "time and gravity pay a cosmetic surgeon's mortgage!"

When Michele and I first went apartment-hunting in New York, my wife said that it was like walking down a wind tunnel as everybody that passed us looked as if their cheeks had been pinned back (as it turned out, they probably had). As we passed the famous Plaza Hotel I realized that we were strolling through a plastic surgeons' paradise, where 60, 70 and 80-somethings shuffled along, defying age with every step. I thought they looked great!

That same day I sat on a bench in the park while Michele went off to get us a couple of coffees and started chatting to the lady next to me. I steered the subject on to plastic surgery and asked if she would ever consider having any work done, suspecting that she already had.

"Getting plastic surgery is like taking care of a car: when it gets a bump or loses its shine, you polish it; when it gets scratched, you get it fixed up - what you do to your face does not change what is beneath the surface." She paused for a moment. "Actually, you know what? That's BS!"

She explained that having the surgery might her feel more like herself if anything because she felt so young. She decided to have a rhinoplasty and a facelift at 55, two years after splitting up with her husband and now every time she looked in the mirror, the image staring back at her now reflected the youthfulness that she felt inside. This applies to your sex-life too and is one reason that society wrongly assumes that older people aren't interesting in sex – appearances can be deceptive and cosmetic surgery can be a way of making you feel more like 'you'.

REMEMBER:

+ Try and be realistic in your expectations – a good surgeon will tell you what to expect while explaining any potential complications fully. Don't put too much stock in a surgeon's before and after photos; they may be more indicative of their talent for doctoring photos than their surgical ability.

+ You may heal more slowly as you age, but because this is the case you are also likely to form less noticeable scars.

CHAPTER 7

BREAKING THE ROUTINE

EVERY experience you have throughout your life is stored in an emotional bank which you will later draw on to sidestep the potholes lurking throughout the next phase. Whether you opt for early-retirement, are forced to retire due to sickness or redundancy, or have been meticulously planning your exit from full-time employment for decades, it is impossible to predict the emotional obstacles awaiting you.

❝❝Do not be too timid and squeamish about your actions. All life is an experience.❞ – *Ralph Waldo Emerson*

However, regardless of your personal circumstances the positive mindset you will need to overcome these obstacles remains the same; the confidence you need to build to adapt to the transition is the same; and the self-belief you need to know that you are entitled to be happy, healthy, attractive and loved is also – you guessed it - the same.

You may find that following the advice on having a great sex-life and boosting your health in retirement through focusing on 'that magic three' becomes impossibly difficult because of the stresses surrounding the lead up to retirement, the actual process of leaving

115

work and adapting your own lifestyle and your relationship to these changes.

After selling my business I did a great job of staying positive for about twenty minutes, before remembering that there was still five days to go before the dreaded event; the night that confirms that you did actually retire, and it wasn't all just a strange and terrifying dream: the retirement party...

So sorry to hear you're leaving... Party Time!

Parties usually conjure up happy images of people laughing, dancing, drinking, leering and doing things which they will later regret, deny and/or apologize for - sometimes in writing if it's something really bad. That's why we all love a good party! We have parties for everything: religious occasions, birthdays, baby showers, weddings, anniversaries and even wakes. The retirement party is more traumatic than all of these put together.

I have discussed these dreaded celebrations with numerous people and reactions ranged from mild irritation to extreme anxiety. Many couldn't bear the constant handshaking and back-slapping. My advice to those of you who feel the same is that you should be able to choose how you want to end your career. If you prefer the fond farewells to remain low-key, then let people know; if some people don't agree with your choices so be it – it's your party and they can cry if they want to.

Be prepared

Don't be naïve enough to think that parties are about relaxing, having fun, or simply turning up and enjoying yourself. Party preparation must be carried out with military precision so that all eventualities have been anticipated well in advance.

The retiree traditionally receives a gift on behalf of their colleagues and very often they are asked what they would like. If they insist on not buying you a real present like a gift voucher for a shop you've never heard of, tell them you only accept cash, major credit cards or cashier's check.

One lady I spoke to asked for a subscription to a popular dating agency as a joke, but didn't find it quite so funny when that's what she received. The present turned out to be a blessing as she had been single for 15 years and ended up marrying her very first date! Retirement really was the start of something new for her.

In some cases colleagues and employers do not ask you what you want. You get what you're given and have to accept it graciously, even if you plan on flogging it on eBay later on.

Garish gifts

a. Generic porcelain figurines. Who actually likes these dust-collecting eyesores? Your colleagues say it is something to remember them by, and if they are vapid and lifeless then perhaps they are the perfect presents.

b. A book of popular country walks. I don't claim to be an expert rambler but I've walked enough over the years to know how to put a pair of shoes on and follow a footpath until I make the executive decision to stop when I'm tired.

c. Landscape painting (usually drab watercolors). These make particularly unpopular presents because they always depict a dreary day. You need cheering up and that does not involve staring wistfully at a rainy landscape asking yourself where it all went wrong.

If you want your gift to make a proper impact, why not use a little imagination and go for something a little bit more risqué...

Sex it up

+ Pay for a bungee jump so that the recipient feels obliged to do it - particularly if you don't like them

+ The Karma Sutra for making the most of all that 'free' leisure time.

+ A novelty 'good buy tension, hello pension' T-shirt from cafeexpress.co.uk

+ How about a risqué crowd-pleaser, like a rampant rabbit for the soon-to-be-retiree. And last but not least...

+ A copy of this book – or ten for all your friends.

The Speech

The party has been an unbridled success. There you are holding your unopened parting gift and listening to your colleague making a terrific speech, showering you with unfamiliarly glowing praise. You're an indispensable work horse, a titan of industry without whom the company will surely fall to pieces in a matter of days!

The applause is thunderous; people clap and cheer in between the clinking of glasses before calling for a speech from their departing friend. You would be feeling fantastic if it didn't strike you as unnervingly like eavesdropping on your own eulogy. How are you meant to respond?

There's always the irreverent opener to fall back on: "For those of you who don't know my wife, this is Marjorie - please don't laugh."

Don't be surprised if Marjorie doesn't laugh either. It might have seemed like a great idea after a bottle of wine but remember that you are planning to spend the rest of your days with Marjorie and that comment may weigh heavily on your future happiness.

It's best to be fairly reserved and aim for slipping in a joke or two while trying not to offend anyone. Your audience doesn't expect stirring oratory throughout, just keep it brief, leave them liking you and let them carry on drinking.

TEST!

It's time for a short recap in the form of a compulsory test. Based on the previous chapter (and hopefully some commonsense) answer the following questions:

Retirement is:

a.   A wonderful, enviable opportunity for learning, self-discovery and great sex

b.   The end of everything positive in your life.

c.   A sign that you are old and must therefore enjoy backgammon, bridge and golf

Bob from accounting, (the guy who stole that promotion you'd been waiting 10 years for), makes a snide comment as you go to shake his hand what do you do?

a.   Smile and say "I'm going to miss that sense of humor Bob, stay in touch!

b.   Squeeze Bob's hand and tell him what you really think of him.

   c.   Anonymously email photos of Bob's conference antics to his boss

You've always had a bit of a thing for the perky 25-year-old blonde who works on reception. You're tipsy and she propositions you by the photocopier, what do you do?

   a.   Tell her that you are flattered but, as a happily married man, must decline

   b.   Take her through the potentially serious risks of direct exposure to ultraviolet light

   c.   Take her over the photocopier and press the green button for a touching memento

You have just delivered a first-rate speech when you are presented with your parting gift. You carefully remove the wrapping paper to reveal a drab watercolor, what do you do?

   a.   Tell them you love it behind gritted teeth

   b.   Ask if they kept the receipt

   c.   Throw it at Bob and wipe that knowing grin of his face

Answers: Obviously 'a.' for all of them. If you got any wrong then repeat the test – it should be easier now that you know the answers.

If nothing else, remember that spiteful verbal tirades aren't generally considered good networking practice. Even if you don't feel like it, try and exude confidence and optimism, suppress any bitter thoughts about your soon-to-be-ex-colleagues and retain your dignity. That means no drunken dancing on tables, lots of smiling (until it hurts), and keeping your speech light and inoffensive.

REMEMBER: Depending on how you want to reinvent yourself in retirement, you may want to get back into part-time work at some point and public insults, however well-delivered are not advisable.

The morning after...

After wallowing for a couple of weeks, getting over the monumental hangover and talking things through with my infinitely patient wife Michele, I had a lapse in confidence. Hazy memories of the retirement party began to float into focus and I pictured rows of colleagues chain-drinking black coffee and poring over spreadsheets – but still I envied them. They had purpose. What did I have?

I hobbled into the bathroom and turned the shaving mirror to the magnifying side to notice a new hair sprouting from my right ear – great, another one.

"Just pull yourself together Larry" I say out loud: "I am still young!", "this is the next phase; I am still sexy!"

This might seem like the behavior of a slightly unhinged person going through a mid-life crisis, but it's what I needed to hear and it does help. Positive affirmations restore your self-confidence and it's amazing how easily you can manipulate your own mindset just by saying these things out loud – don't let skepticism jeopardize your retirement happiness.

The line of equilibrium

The 'Line of Equilibrium' is a simple method of visualizing how we need to respond dynamically to significant life-changes if our relationship is to absorb the impact of the next phase and move forward.

The line begins when you meet somebody new and enter a relationship. It is flat to represent the stress level of our everyday lives, but as we reach an important life-event, it spikes, representing the extra strain exerted on our relationship. A new plane must be drawn to signify that a negotiated position has been reached.

Once your relationship has adapted, the line continues along this plane until you make another important life-decision. In a moment of madness you might decide to get married, or even re-married; the line spikes like crazy as you have to re-evaluate your aims and redraw the bounds of your relationship. As with marriage or having a child, retirement is a significant (and sometimes painful) life-event, but the difference is, it is far too frequently overlooked. Often retirees (including myself) are simply in denial, or take a blinkered view of the next phase, only choosing to publically acknowledge the positive aspects of the transition – i.e. "fantastic - no more early-mornings!" while secretly dreading workplace withdrawal.

Everybody knows to expect a period of grief or bereavement when somebody close to them dies. What people don't realize is that bereavement can affect any loss situation – including the loss of your job through retirement, regardless of whether you have been made redundant or opt for early retirement. As with any intensely stressful situation the symptoms of job bereavement vary from person to person but typically include a combination of:

+ Isolation

+ Low self-esteem

+ Anger

+ Depression

There are many methods that you can adopt to counter these debilitating emotions, but something that helped me enormously was the use of regular affirmations.

Affirmations are positive aphorisms, affirmations are positive aphorisms, affirm...

Affirmations are positive aphorisms repeated out loud to condition your sub-conscious, dispelling any niggles that will prevent you from reaching your full potential, and allowing you to feel happy, healthy, attractive and loved. Unsurprisingly, the most effective affirmations are those which are affirming. Replace phrases such as 'I will' or even 'I can' - which imply an intention in the future - with 'I am' to reinforce your present state – eventually your mood will take the hint.

Instead of saying: "I will be happy and successful", say "I am happy and successful!", and mean it (even if you don't necessarily believe it). You might feel ridiculous at first but it gets easier.

REMEMBER: Cynicism might make you feel clever, but it never made anyone any happier – and no-one likes a smart-ass.

Affirmations should be said first thing in the morning to put you in the right mindset for the rest of the day. Each should be repeated a minimum of 20 times, slowly and with feeling as you visualize the positive effects; find a quiet, tranquil place where you won't be disturbed. Take your time. Relax.

Affirmations can be targeted at specific areas of your life or characteristics where you feel you are especially lacking; for example, if you want to build your self-confidence and self-belief try these affirmations:

+ I am growing every day

+ I have faith in my inner-strength

+ Fear of failure does not hold me back

If body issues are your primary concern then what about these? (You may have to try particularly hard to suspend your disbelief here), but believe me, it works:

+ My body feels light and healthy

+ I am healthy in body, mind and spirit

+ My body is filled with energy

As you become more comfortable with the process of repeating your affirmations, and attuned to their meaning, try developing your own targeted affirmations to work on your own personal insecurities. Do not allow niggling doubts (or 'negative self-talk' as it has been labeled) to deter you. There is nothing wrong with wanting to feel happy, and you shouldn't feel guilty for empowering yourself and looking on the bright side of life!

Negativity and cynicism are often viewed as a more realistic and mature approach to life than positivity, but this thinking is both counter-intuitive and counter-productive. If you want to be happy, concentrate on you and disregard unhelpful criticism. This may seem self-centerd but remember that you must be happy to radiate positive energy and maximize your impact on those around you.

Walking the relationship tightrope

As the majority of couples retire at different times, the dynamics of your relationship are liable to change unexpectedly, throwing up many new challenges. This can lead to impinging on each other's role, breaking tacit agreements that form the foundation of your relationship and heading straight for relationship meltdown if your issues are not communicated openly and honestly.

The kids had grown up and moved away and Michele was confident about the future. Her self-assurance made me even more conscious of my own lack of direction. She later admitted that her greatest concern at that time was how I was going to cope with the transition (and her greatest irritation was me repeatedly asking her what time she would get home from work).

A 2008 report from the UK government's Department for Work and Pensions (DWP) revealed that the divorce rate in the over-50s has soared by a fifth in the last decade, despite a 16 percent overall drop in the divorce rate during this period. The report suggests that this can be partially explained by the high likelihood of the children having flown the nest by this point, leading to the woman spending more time with their recently retired partner, and deciding that they are looking for someone else (specifically, almost anybody who isn't their husband).

The tragedy is that the rewards of staying together for longer are great – and not just in the intangible emotional sense but in terms of your sex-life too: experience = expertise.

Because the stability of our closest relationships lies at the center of our happiness in retirement, the next step in my journey was to visit a relationship counsellor to get some practical tips for surviving the transition period intact.

Retired Spouse Syndrome

The fallout of retirement affects those around you just as much, if not more, than yourself. Relationships are based on precise dynamics that are embedded deep in your daily routine and might have changed little (if at all) in decades. The extent to which retirement may threaten your relationship depends on:

+ Whether one person in the relationship has always been the main breadwinner it can be even more difficult to stop working especially if your partner is younger than yourself, and still putting in the hours.

+ How much time you spent together before retirement and if the answer is 'barely any' then why?

+ How effectively you communicate your feelings to your partner.

The significance of this phenomenon can also vary widely between different cultures. It is estimated that in Japan, 60% of older women experience difficulties when their husbands who were previously working very long hours retire at 60, coining the phrase 'retired husband syndrome' to describe the effects on the physical and mental health of the wife when their husband retires and asserts their authority in the home.

Artistic differences...

Sheila was a talented artist and part-time receptionist who was exasperated when her husband picked up a paintbrush soon after retirement. His monstrous creations gradually spread through the house like an infectious disease, scarring the stylish interior. Although she was frustrated, Sheila couldn't bring herself to hurt her husband's feelings by revealing the extent to which his newfound interest irked her.

The problem was that she felt he had trespassed into an area of her life that she had used as a means of escaping from everyday stresses (incurred mainly through living with him).

Thankfully he lost interest and took up the violin instead. Although Sheila was then subjected to two hours of what sounded like a cat being strangled, it was something she was prepared to put up with, at least for a while. Sharing your partner's interests can be a great way to spend more time together if the decision is mutual, but hijacking them can spell disaster.

REMEMBER: Don't be offended if your partner is protective over their interests; you do not have to do everything together, pursuing separate activities is healthy and can ultimately bring you closer in retirement.

Although the importance of communication cannot be stressed highly enough, it is crucial to acknowledge the general differences between how men and women often approach these issues, seek support and advice, and work towards a solution as outlined most famously in John Gray's relationship bible, *Men Are from Mars, Women Are from Venus*.

Men are essentially 'fixers', they have an instinctive drive to fix problems but more often than not, it's not a quick-fix that women are after. Men deal with problems by slinking off and mulling them over by themselves until they have reached a solution (or come to the unlikely conclusion that they need to seek help). Women, on the other-hand often yearn for emotional support as an end in itself.

It is often helpful to step back and give your partner the breathing space they need. If your husband comes to the same conclusion that you suggested three days previously saying: "I told you that 3 days ago!" is neither tactful nor advisable. And, of course, generalisations, however useful, money-spinning or amusing in a kind of anachronistic sexist way are no substitute for remaining sensitive to your partner's individual needs.

Redrawing boundaries

Daniel's wife had multiple sclerosis and would always leave a list of chores including the weekly shopping when she was feeling particularly unwell. He knew when she was feeling better because any offer to help would be met with a swift and expletive-laden response.

The key to ensuring that you reach a negotiated position with your partner is that both sides are taken into account at every stage. The way you interact with each other is an unspoken contract which you may not be aware of right up until you break one of the unspoken clauses and have to pay the price. For example, if the wife is getting sick of tidying the house twice as much now that you are retired, any discussion that ensues should not be cynically or selfishly motivated.

REMEMBER: 'Sharing' does not mean strategically holding onto the chores you dislike the least whilst offloading those you loathe. Discussion shouldn't descend into a game of relationship battleships as this is of no benefit to anyone and usually leads to a far longer game of solitaire.

The solution is communication. It's natural and healthy to have these thoughts providing you share your anxieties with your partner. Sometimes the most important thing is giving your spouse the space they need. Allowing your partner to pursue their own interests and develop outside of the relationship ensures that the time you spend together will not be as fraught or frustrating:

+ Sit down and discuss any concerns with your partner
  Although this can be extremely difficult, it is a crucial first step, and will help allay future conflicts bringing you closer together.

+ Personalize your plans
  This doesn't mean excluding your partner from the decision-making process, but a happy retirement means being honest about what you want from the beginning.

+ Ask for help
  Don't be afraid to share your concerns with friends and family, or seek professional advice. A neutral environment can help you see things more clearly.

+ Communication is key
  It may sound trite, but it's also true. Retirement is no time for second-guessing your partner and besides, it's good to talk.

+ Empathize don't criticize
  Remember that a little constructive criticism tactfully delivered can be helpful, but don't let the conversation turn into a slanging match.

Sometimes with the best will in the world, space won't necessary produce the results you are looking for, even though the outcome will ultimately benefit your retirement later on. Some of the revelations that accompany retirement aren't always positive but you need to accept them and move on. My next interviewee had first-hand experience of this...

Crossing the line

Michael worked in an oil company until its acquisition by a large American conglomerate that whittled down the workforce and offered everybody over the age of 55 the choice of a modest redundancy package or retraining for a role in a different department. As he had been dreaming about retirement for years and the offer conveniently coincided with his wife, Linda's promotion to office manager, he accepted.

Linda still worked three days a week, but retirement meant they would be able to spend more quality time together. She came up with the idea of making every Monday 'date night' to keep the romance in their relationship alive.

At first, things were great. Michael kept himself busy with long-overdue DIY projects and, while the place was starting to look like a show home, even Monday nights became dull and unpredictable; they weren't spending any other quality time together and conversation usually ended in one of them walking into another room.

"One day, after one of our usual rows Linda told me that she was sick of seeing me loafing around the house" Michael says. "We had a huge row where we both said things we didn't mean. I slept on the sofa and the next day we carried on as if nothing had happened but it was still playing on my mind." A couple of weeks later, after the best night out we'd had in months, we got home, opened a nice bottle of wine and Linda said she fancied an early night. She practically dragged me into the bedroom, but then it happened - or didn't" Michael says.

"What happened?" I ask. "Do I need to spell it out? I couldn't get an erection. Linda was upset, and, even though she said it didn't matter, I could see that she was disappointed and it really got to me. It happened again a couple of nights later and then the following week," he says. "I just couldn't understand it. I'm not claiming to be some sort of Casanova, but I've never had any problems in that department before."

Michael booked an appointment with his doctor who asked him whether he ever woke up with an erection... yes, was he still masturbating, yes... had he been through any stressful circumstances recently, etc. The doctor diagnosed the problem as psychogenic rather than physical impotence and suggested that the couple considered relationship counseling. When Michael raised the issue later on she told him that she wouldn't be able to come as the appointment clashed with an unavoidable business trip.

Visiting that counselor was the first time he had actually spoken about any of his relationship anxieties to anybody other than Linda.

"When I got back home Linda was still out, so I waited up for her. By the time she eventually got home, just after midnight, I felt strangely calm. I could smell the alcohol on her breath which was strange as she barely ever drank - except for the odd glass of wine with dinner. I don't know what made me say it. I had never even thought about it up to that point but I just came out and asked if she was having an affair."

"There was no protest. She just looked at me and started welling up. She had been having an affair for two years; the so called client-visit was a cover-up while she spent the night in a hotel with her boss – all while I was trying to save our marriage."

Michael packed his bags the next morning and moved out that day. It was tragic to think that this man's 35-year marriage had broken up only a year after the strains of the transition into retirement had finally taken their toll.

REMEMBER

+ Although we may retire alone, the fall-out from the transition can affect relationships with those around you, particularly your spouse. Be mindful of this and give your relationship time to adjust.

+ Be patient when children and friends give you advice. Remember they usually have your best interests at heart.

+ Above all, keep the lines of communication open. Talk to your spouse, talk to your family, talk to a professional counsellor. Whoever it is, talk to somebody! A short and momentarily painful conversation will help clear the way for your future happiness and ensure your personal well-being throughout the next phase.

CHAPTER 8

REINVENTING
YOURSELF

THE *freedom that retirement offers makes working out how to spend your leisure time a surprisingly traumatic ordeal. The problem is rooted in the abundance of choice that characterizes the modern age. Research led by psychologist Barry Schwartz challenged the traditional paradigm that 'more is better' through, for example, discovering that the more retirement plans a company offers, the fewer employees take out a plan - (unfortunately companies know this too and have boosted the number of retirement plans they offer accordingly).*

The paradoxical idea that more choices can lead to bad decisions, stress and despair is especially relevant at transitional phases in your life which demand a level of decisiveness – retirement is no exception.

It isn't just potentially life-changing decisions that are affected by this paradox of choice, but everyday living where the simplest tasks have become a slog: from not knowing what to order at a restaurant with three separate menus to deciding what toothpaste to buy. The stress accompanying so-called 'convenience living' is one of the greatest threats to your retirement happiness - but there is hope my fellow Baby Boomers...

Your perfect retirement picture

Retirement books stress the importance of visualizing the next phase as a blank canvas with a palette of paints representing your various leisure activities, interests; family commitments etc. - I advise you not to, because it isn't like that at all.

"To be able to fill leisure intelligently is the last product of civilization." –
Bertrand Russell

You should already have an idea about your likes and dislikes, but that isn't to say that you shouldn't try new things and put yourself out of your comfort zone. In the same way that you need to vary your sex-life to keep things interesting, so must you keep an open-mind when it comes to working out what to do with all that leisure-time. Stamp-collecting may not strike you as your idea of a great night in, but you won't know for sure unless you try it.

Think of your future as a sliding tile puzzle and the end-picture as your perfect retirement. Half of the tiles are already filled in with your current leisure activities, interests, work aspirations and family commitments. The other half are like blank scrabble tiles. These 'wild' tiles can be filled in and moved into position once you have thrown yourself into new activities and found out what works, what doesn't and what you're itching to try again.

"Do not do unto others as you would that they should do unto you. Their tastes may not be the same" –
George Bernard Shaw

Retirement gives you the freedom and autonomy to be spontaneous. If you want to lie-in on a Monday morning you can. If you want to walk around the house smoking Cuban cigars in nothing but a dragon-print kimono for a week, then I might question your taste in home casual-wear, but it's your call. The likelihood is, you won't want to do this because, a. Cuban cigars are expensive (and illegal in America), and b. If you read the small-print that comes with this newfound freedom in retirement, you'll see that it is bundled with an unavoidable element of guilt. This is because we are conditioned to attach certain attributes to the concepts of 'work' and 'leisure' which must be abandoned if we are to make the most of our golden years.

Work and Leisure: two sides of the same coin

Try a quick word association exercise. Write down the words 'work' and 'leisure' in two columns and spend a couple of minutes jotting down associations with each. I asked 30 retirees to do the same and the results revealed a surprising crossover. 'Achievement', 'team-work', 'responsibility', 'reward' and 'goals' are integral to our overall happiness in whatever we are doing,

> **"Time you enjoy wasting, was not wasted." –**
> *John Lennon*

but years of work impresses upon us the idea that we are somehow being unproductive or lazy if we're not crammed together in a grey office building drinking watery coffee.

The leisure activities that we enjoy the most in retirement are those which most effectively satisfy the positive aspects of work (i.e. the parts that we actually miss) and these are also the activities that will make us happiest. The boundary between these aspects is not rigid, e.g. taking tennis lessons and taking part in a tournament (even if you are thrashed in the first round) will encompass feelings of **accomplishment, competition, community and learning.**

As we saw with Maslow's hierarchy of needs in Chapter 1, employment is one of the most fundamental needs leading to happiness, on the second rung just above physiological needs. If we can replace the positive elements of work with leisure - and that nearly never includes watching the TV which is known to reduce happiness - maintain a wide 'social convoy' as we age and enjoy a healthy sex-life, then we will continue to grow in retirement.

A world away from work

If the idea of applying for jobs, mopping up your tears with handfuls of rejection letters and putting yourself through the traumatic process of preparing for interview falls between petting a tarantula and having root canal treatment in your top 10 list of 'things you would least like to do' then you will be relieved to hear that, yes, there is a world outside the workplace which many of my interviewees were elated to discover in later life.

> **"Retirement without the love of letters is a living burial." –**
> *Seneca*

In a working environment you usually come into contact with all age groups. When you retire you miss that mix. Make an attempt to meet all age groups either through voluntary service, part-time work or special interest groups of your own. Do you play the guitar? Do you like computers? Join a club! Even pursuits that you think you hate are worthy trying again now that you are doing them out of choice. Believe it or not, even returning to education can be a rewarding pastime in retirement...

Educating Peter

Peter worked as a warehouse operative for a large retailer where he drove a mini-forklift, unloading deliveries and unpacking boxes for thirty years. It was physically demanding work; repetitive and low-paid. But he knew what was expected, always exceeded his targets and never had to worry about taking responsibility for anybody else's mistakes.

"I turned down the move up to supervisor more times than I can remember" says Peter. "They were always trying to push that one on me."

I contact Peter after a tip from one of the lawyers who hurried along the sale of my business. Peter had a history of back pain and arthritis after years of strenuous lifting, but everything changed after an accident at work.

"I was off-loading a shipment of TVs," he says. "It wasn't the weight of them – they were just awkward to carry. We were working to tight deadlines and it was a Friday so we all wanted to get home. I carried the box a few steps, slipped on the wet concrete floor and landed on my back with the full weight of the box on top of me. The cleaners had been mopping but there were no safety cones around.

"I had to have a lot of physio - the doctors said it was a miracle I could still walk. I had pins and needles and a strange numb feeling in my left leg running down into my foot. I had to have a few x-rays and an MRI scans - they told me I'd slipped a disc and wouldn't be able to go back to work."

His seniors immediately went on the defensive so Peter sought legal advice and sued the company. The process was long and tedious, but his side assured him that his case was sound and it was more a question of 'how much?' than anything else.

"I ended up with more than £200,000, but I had to have a couple of operations privately and still might have to have another one. I don't know how the wife has put up with it."

This couple were happier being interviewed about their experiences separately and Peter's wife, Jane shed a lot more light on how much the situation had affected her husband.

"He was popular, played darts in a local league and was always the comedian in the crowd, but after the accident his personality changed overnight. He would sit around the house and go quiet – that's how you know something's wrong with Peter; the wall goes up and there's no getting through. I think it was a bit of everything: the accident, not seeing his friends, the slow recovery and so on. I had depression when our son Steven was three, and I saw the same signs in him – I practically had to beg him to go and see someone."

Peter eventually agreed and was prescribed anti-depressants by his doctor which didn't seem to help.

"He picked up a little bit so I decided to book us a surprise vacation, a fortnight in Andalusia at a fully-catered hotel. We hadn't been away for years. It was a disaster to begin with. I had looked into where we could go, restaurants and bars, and tried to keep the energy up but he wanted to stay in the room. I ended up doing my own thing. Our sex-life had gone from bad to worse. He wouldn't even look at me."

I wanted to hear Peter's take on things. It was clear from many of the couples I had already spoken to that each person in the relationship can differ greatly in how they identify the root cause of an issue. It is vital to establish where these differing perspectives converge and build on this commonality.

Peter agreed that he hadn't exactly been the life and soul of the party after the accident, but focused more on the turning-point of the trip – the penultimate night where he began to view his prospects in a more positive light.

"I went to the bar and began chatting to the guy I was sitting next to you. He came from the midlands somewhere and used to work for the council – Geoff his name was. I told him about the accident and once I started, didn't shut up until I'd told him everything. He asked me what I was going to do when I got home and I can't remember exactly what I said, something about looking for part-time work - the truth was I hadn't even thought about it. I'm not one for complaining but I felt like I'd given up on everything at that point."

Geoff said that he should consider taking some kind of course "I was kicked out of more subjects than I passed at school but I thought about it and with a bit of persuasion decided to give it a go. I was miserable anyway so I had to do something." He ended up enrolling on an engineering night class and surprised himself with the ease at which he was picking it all up.

I asked him how all of this affected his sex-life and he reluctantly admitted that he had lost interest in sex and had been unable to achieve an erection. He went to the doctor who suspected that it might be linked to the anti-depressants he had been prescribed. After tapering off them, Peter was put on something different and lo-and-behold the situation quickly improved.

"We're a different couple now." Peter says. "I still get occasional pain in my back and legs, especially if we're out and about, but I still see the lads from work and after taking a few computer classes I decided that I wanted to try and get an engineering degree through the Open University. I never would have dreamed of doing something that before, and I can tell you, I've had some funny looks when I tell people but it turns out that I'm not quite as hopeless as I thought."

> **❝Education is learning what you didn't even know you didn't know.❞** –
> *Daniel J. Boorstin*

Whether you are interested in returning to education to get some letters after your name or just for the experience of learning about a subject that has always interested you there are a number of options to consider:

The Open University offers over 600 university-level courses in more than 60 subjects. You can take part in distant-learning from the comfort of your own home and there are a huge number of over-60s reaping the benefits of learning in later life. Decades of full-time work mean that mature students often have a more disciplined work-ethic – but the syllabus itself is only half of the story. The learning environment is a social platform too, giving you the opportunity to meet new like-minded people and make friends through joining online study groups.

If you are more attracted to the community element of learning rather than the certificate at the end of it, the **University of the Third Age (U3A)** could be more up your street. Despite sounding like a sinister New Age cult, U3A is a great organisation made up of and run by more than 250,000 people in individual learning cooperatives around the UK. Each cooperative is different but U3A offers a total of 300 subjects in such fields as art, life sciences, computing and walking.

Across the Pond

In the US, the majority of universities have Continuing Education departments offering mature students the opportunity to return to learning, whether the goal is working towards an accredited qualification, topping up existing skills, or discovering something completely new. The School of Continuing and Professional Studies at **New York University** for example offers more than 4,000 courses spanning every subject imaginable. If you're already comfortable with the internet then there are online universities such as **University of Phoenix** which offers online degree programs; if not, maybe you should consider taking a computing qualification first!

Returning to education is not for everyone and I encountered people who had taken courses, thrown themselves into it and realized it wasn't for them - Greg was one such retiree. This experience is not wasted. It is by trying these different options that you can start to fill in those 'wild' tiles and bring your perfect retirement picture into focus.

❝ ❝ Knowledge is the food of the soul. ❞ – *Plato*

Greg Thomson was more prepared than most for retirement. His mortgage was paid and he started paying into a pension in his early-twenties and now qualified for the full state pension in addition to his private investments. Greg came from a typical working-class background, his father, Patrick, worked in a steel factory all of his life while his mother stayed at home and took care of him and his two brothers.

Greg's father died at 53 of a coronary thrombosis and although he was a promising student, Greg was forced to drop his dream of being the first person in their family to go to university and concentrate on bringing in the household income. He was very well-read and a brief tour of his home revealed stacks of dusty books piled up to the ceiling in every corner.

I read about Greg in local paper that ran a story about residents of retirement age getting involved with the community, and made contact with him through one of the volunteering organizations with which he was involved. "So how did it all start?" I ask.

"I've never been a religious man by any stretch of the imagination" Greg replies, "but I sometimes go to Church on a Saturday for a second-hand book sale, and one morning I spotted a poster advertising a six-week beginners' computer course. I guess you could say I was a technophobe so I wanted to prove to myself that I could do it. The teacher was clearly passionate about her subject, and incredibly patient, but some people just couldn't grasp what she was saying - it was frustrating sitting there for twenty minutes at a time doing nothing."

"One of the most positive aspects of taking computer classes was that it turned out to be a great way to meet new people in the area – even if there didn't seem to be a noticeable improvement in my computer skills. We went out for lunch in the second or possibly third week of the course and I met a woman called Sandra whose son worked for the tourist bureau. She gave me his number and I managed to arrange some volunteering work, giving guided tours of local landmarks. I was never much of a public speaker and they were probably the most incoherent tours in history – but it was good fun trying something new."

Greg went back to the drawing board and brainstormed other areas where he thought he could put his skills to most use. He found the number of the volunteers' co-ordinator at a local hospital on the internet. "She initially mentioned working in the tea-shop in the out-patients' clinic, but I wanted something more involved than that. Unfortunately they couldn't offer anything else and I felt like my heart had to be in whatever I settled for otherwise I wouldn't enjoy it and that was important to me as well."

"The son of one of the ladies on the computer course was an English teacher in a school nearby. He told me about a volunteering initiative where retirees could come in for an afternoon and help children with basic literacy and numeracy" he says. "I asked for his contact details and gave him a call later that day. First they wanted me to read to the children, taking them through some basic exercises and talking to them about any of the books that they had read – that sounded like something I could do. Although I didn't get my degree, the thought of making a difference to somebody else's education seemed just as rewarding."

Hidden talents often emerge with a change of occupation and Greg proved to be a natural teacher. He ended up having to drop some of his commitments to make way for extended family and just to get some time out for himself. This is a sign that Greg really had built up a clear picture of his perfect retirement and was making the most of his later years.

❝❝ Happiness is not something ready-made. It comes from your own actions." – *Dalai Lama*

If you're giving just to make yourself happier, but you are making people happier anyway, does that still make you selfish? I have a feeling that I might have stolen that perennial philosophical dilemma from an episode of Friends - but I digress.

If you've decided to volunteer then here's a short guide to finding the right role for you...

G.I.V.E. – A mini-guide to volunteering

Get out there!

So you've decided that volunteering is something in which you are interested – that's great, but now you need to look at your options. There will usually be a volunteer bureau in your city which is essentially a job-shop for unpaid work. As usual, the internet should be your first port of call and sites such as www.vinspired.com and www.volunteermatch.org are great starting points.

Don't forget local business directories, community centers, notice-boards in supermarkets, malls, religious institutions or even just word-of-mouth recommendations from friends and family (even if they have no direct volunteering experience, it's likely that someone will be able to point you in the right direction).

Involve yourself

Once you have done some research you need to consider the level of involvement to which you are prepared to commit. In order to ensure that you get the most of your experience, and put your time, energy and skills to best use, you need to ask yourself the following questions:

- How many hours/days per week are you available?

- Are you prepared to work weekends or evenings?

- Would you like to work on your own or as part of a team?

- What kind of work are you looking for?

+ Is your main focus to learn and make new friends, or just to help the community?

+ Do you have any physical/mental impairment that may render you unsuitable for certain positions?

Variety

There are volunteering opportunities in every sector catering for all manner of interests, but if you're struggling for ideas here are a few to get you started:

Community	Charity	Environment
Clothes/food banks, soup kitchens, youth clubs, community centers, hospitals, schools, museums, prisons	American Cancer Society, The Samaritans, homeless shelters, United Way, McMillan Cancer Relief, The Salvation Army	The National Trust, Friends of the Earth, national parks, Greenpeace, animal conservation

There are plenty of more left-field opportunities as well if you look hard enough; always been told you've had a face for radio? Give it a try! Hospital radio is a great way to dust off your LPs and make a difference to someone's day – don't let that self-doubt hold you back.

Enjoyment

If you want to feel good, do something good for somebody else but remember that this is your retirement, and your leisure time to spend exactly how you wish. So, if you aren't enjoying it, move on to something else.

Thanks Larry that's great! (But I still want to go back to work)...

If you find the lure of work too irresistible, then you're not alone. In a book about retirement and the effect it has on our relationships and sex-life I could see how you might be on the verge of throwing this book in disgust and shouting 'you sell-out Larry, why are you talking about work again?' But the truth is that some people are so used to the routine that comes with a career that they just can't replace that work-shaped hole in their life (or their bank balance). To feel happy in yourself, and radiate happiness in your relationships, it may be necessary to return to the world of drinks fountains, name badges and pond-water masquerading as coffee - and that's fine too...

A survey carried out by one of the UK's largest insurance companies, Norwich Union showed that 44% of people aged between 65 and 74 return to work in some capacity; whether full-time, part-time or within the voluntary sector. Of these people only 14% return to work because they need the money and 27% opted for voluntary work.

There are numerous recruitment agencies specializing in placing older people in jobs, most of which take their names from the amusing symbolism associated with aging:

- wrinklies DIRECT (www.wrinklies.org)

- www.seniorjobbank.org (okay, not this one)

- Dinosaurs Unlimited – (www.dinosaursunlimited.co.uk)

These agencies all stress that you should not be discouraged from looking for work because of a lengthy period of unemployment, or because you feel your age puts you at a disadvantage – remember that experience also means expertise and the knowledge that you have built up over the years is a highly-valued asset.

MYTH: You can't teach an old dog new tricks.

FACT: You can teach an old dog new tricks.

If you want to find work there are always avenues to explore, agencies willing to help and employers eager to take you on – there is nothing stopping you except yourself. You just need the tenacity of our old friend the professor and the grit of my next interviewee, Anne.

New beginnings

Anne went to secretarial college and struck me as being the student who always had her hand up first, and was nearly always right. After the course, she took various secretarial roles before being headhunted for the job of personal assistant to the finance director of an auditing firm. She was clearly a methodical woman. Everything Anne did was exacting down to the symmetry of the tea and Battenberg cake laid out in front of me.

"I've worked hard my whole life" she says. "That's just what you did; that's what my parents did. I wasn't worried about being the most popular person in the office – don't get me wrong I did have friends, but work was work" she says.

I ask her why she retired. "My husband – ex-husband - Derek and I had always planned it that way. I'd had a tough couple of years after the other PA resigned and her workload was passed on to me - for no extra money of course. It got to the point where I had savings and I just asked myself why I was putting myself through it all when I didn't have to."

"It wasn't until I retired that I noticed anything was wrong at all." Anne says. "We had never been one of those touchy-feely couples anyway. I made Derek's dinner every night, ironed his shirts every morning and we rarely argued. But by then it had become more of a living arrangement than a marriage.

"We never had children, but my elder brother lives down south with his wife and their daughter Natalie, and I wanted to be closer to them after I retired. I started going to a reading group and meeting new people. I was busy making plans for the future and it might sound callous, but it was difficult to work out where Derek came into that.

"It turned out I needn't have worried. It wasn't quite lipstick on the collar, but not far off" she says. "He left his mobile phone at home one day by accident. He came back to the house at lunch-time to pick it up but I had already read his messages. There were pages of them. Texts from a woman he had talked about in the past, a supervisor less than half his age, with names of hotels along with the kinds of things that he used to say to me 30 years ago.

"It only confirmed what we both already knew: our relationship was already over; we just hadn't broken up yet. He had been seeing one of his young supervisors. I confronted him, we had a big row and I told him to leave. That was two years ago now and we're still going through the legal motions to get a divorce but we haven't spoken face to face for months."

After Derek left, Anne started looking for part-time work almost straight away. They planned on pooling their finances but now that the relationship was over Anne wanted to return to work. "I applied for a few jobs before I heard anything. I was eventually invited for an interview at the public library where I would be archiving journals and doing some general admin. It's only three days a week but that gives me a chance to relax when I need to and read the rest of the time."

Anne was almost pious in her self-sufficiency, but was she happy? Did she secretly yearn for companionship and intimacy? It's not for me to speculate (but I don't think so). Like any important life-event: an illness, a death, having a child etc., retirement can serve as a catalyst, revealing any frailties in our relationships and forcing us to confront them head-on, whether we want to or not

On the other side of the spectrum was Matthew. He worked his way up the ranks to become European Operations Director of one of the largest packaging companies in the world. While he was a successful businessman, this strategic insight didn't translate into his retirement planning. During my research I found that the more successful the interviewee (in terms of seniority in their occupation) were generally more ill-prepared for the next phase. I think even he would admit that he would have been lost without the help of his resilient wife, Meghan.

Matthew's business achievements and charity work led to significant coverage in local and regional business press making the loss of status that accompanied his retirement an even more bitter pill to swallow.

Although he was only 62 and had no imminent plans to retire, Matthew had been pushed out of the organization by the Chairman who wanted to reshape the organization and bring in some new blood.

"I saw it as a personal clash rather than anything professional" he says. "He had always taken more of a backseat, but the dynamics shifted, everything I did was scrutinized to the point where I didn't feel able to do my job properly. Technically speaking I wasn't fired, but they didn't give me much of a choice either. I was offered a generous payoff and could have taken it to a tribunal, but I've been caught up in those proceedings before and didn't want to have to deal with that kind of stress on top of everything else."

Recognizing something of my own situation in Matthew's story made me eager to find out more. I wanted to know how he had handled the transition from big business to retirement and basically whether he made as much of a mess of it as I had in the beginning...

"I wanted to go back to work straightaway. I do have other interests: I'm in a squash league, I joined the Rotary club and occasionally play online chess – badly. Our home-life is still busy with my daughter and her two young children living less than a mile away but I was surprised how tough it was."

"Matthew's frustration spilled over into our home life" Meghan says. I never realized that retirement would affect all of us – not just him. When he stopped working you could see that he didn't know what to do next. Alison, our daughter, would bring around the kids for him to look after during the day and he was even picking them up from school three times a week for the first couple of months."

"I love being a grandfather" Matthew says. "But when you feel like it is expected of you, it starts to become a chore rather than a pleasure - you try telling that to a house full of women.

"I knew I had to get back into work. I contacted a few friends in the City and was invited to interview for a non-executive role in another manufacturing company. I thought it went very well, and because I had known one of the directors for years, I assumed that I would have to do something pretty disastrous to not get the job. On reflection, perhaps it was that assumption that led to complacency – they say pride comes before a fall. Less than a week after the interview I found out that I had been unsuccessful. I asked why and they said that even though I had the experience, I didn't show enough enthusiasm."

I wanted to know how their sex-lives had changed during this time. "I've always been a very sexual person" Meghan laughs. "I did notice a change in the bedroom, actually a couple of months before he retired. I know some couples in turbulent relationships use sex to regain that closeness, but we definitely weren't one of them. The problem was never physical either; we were just so short with each other that neither of us was ever in the mood."

149

"I can see that I was being selfish" Matthew said, "but it's tough to be that objective with the situation when you're going through it, that's why we eventually decided it was best to contact a professional."

The couple eventually booked a few sessions with a relationship counselor to talk things through and try to redefine their roles. It also helped that a couple of months later Matthew was offered a position as a high-level management consultant, an opportunity that led to a successful second post-retirement career – plus he could choose when to work and see Alison and the kids at times that suited both of them rather than feeling obliged.

If you've decided to return to the workplace and have been invited to interview – congratulations! This means that at least one person thinks that you are up to the job, even if everybody else preferred the other guy.

Interviews: Back to Basics

Although you might not have anticipated returning to work, preparation is fundamental to your success regardless of your age, experience or skill-set. Here's a bite size guide to help you get started:

1. The first step is to scour through your application form and your resume to remember what you have written so that you don't panic when they question you about qualifications or experience that you may have inadvertently embellished/ plucked out of thin air.

2. Re-read the job description until you know it inside out. You need to be absolutely clear about what they are looking for so that you can tailor your approach with the employer in mind.

3. Prepare and practice answers to questions to the classic questions:

- **'Why do you want this job?'**
  Make sure your answer highlights the skills you have that they want, (again, check the job description).

- **'What is your greatest weakness?'**
  The following answers are not acceptable:
    - "Umm, high blood pressure?" – No physical ailments.
    - "I always buckle under pressure" – Never admit to an actual weakness.
    - "I don't have any, it's great to be me" – Don't be arrogant.

The right answer is one which deflects the question and emphasizes a positive attribute - like so: "Well, I am a perfectionist, I find it difficult to leave a task unless I am 110% happy with the results!" – Congratulations, you've got the job.

- **'Why do you want to work for <insert company name> in particular?'**
  Regardless of your previous experience, qualifications or party tricks (no matter how impressive), it is essential to research the potential employer. Browsing a company's website, paying particular attention to their history and recent achievements, will make you seem prepared, well-informed and able to take initiative.

For competency-based questions such as: 'Describe a situation where you worked in a team', the **STAR** mnemonic will be your skeleton key to success:

Situation	Where did you last use the competency in question?
Task	What were you tasked with?
Action	What course of action did you take?
Result	What were the direct results of your action(s)?

+ **'Do you have any questions for us?'**

The golden rule here is: never say "no, I think that about does it." Failure to think of at least one reasonable question shows that you are unimaginative at best and, at worst, somebody who isn't concerned about squandering opportunities.

The best response is to follow-up on a topic already broached during the interview. If you are really stuck you could ask specific questions about the potential for advancement, or for a typical 'day in the life' of somebody in the role for which you have applied.

BEWARE: Do not try and be funny as this could backfire, (this also applies to books about reinventing yourself and having great sex in retirement), and avoid asking question that you should already be able to answer such as: "What does the company actually do?"

Ask the most patient person you know to give you a mock interview so that you can practice your model answers. It doesn't matter if the interview doesn't go exactly as expected, adequate preparation will boost your confidence and put you in the positive mindset to adapt and impress, even if you have to improvise.

An unexpected twist

After a three-hour interview with a careers advisor I decided to try and steer the conversation on to positive thinking and how to carry on having a great sex after retirement. She looked taken aback (to say the least) but it soon transpired that she had a surprising story of her own.

Picture the most romantic place you could hope to meet the love of your lie. What are you thinking? A Hawaiian beach with the sound of the ocean and palm trees swaying in the moonlight? An evening stroll down the chans de lise followed by wine and dinner at a rustic French bistro, by moonlight? Not even close.

Joy was only 57, had been single for more than twenty years and was working in a senior management position at the inner-city school that she attended as a child. When one of her old school-friends died she decided to go to the funeral and pay her respects.

It was an emotional occasion, but Joy was reunited with some old school friends, including an ex-boyfriend who she split up with when they went their separate ways to university. The advantage of meeting at a funeral was that neither of them had to pluck up the courage to invite the other out for a drink as they were both heading to the wake afterwards.

This story had a happy ending as the couple were married in under a year and, as far as I know, are still together now. A positive outcome emerging from an otherwise morbid situation, (albeit, still a celebration of a life well-lived), reaffirms the immortal words of Chuck Berry: "you never can tell". So don't make excuses and get out there!

Just do it

However you choose to reinvent your life in retirement: whether through spending more time with your family or travelling with your partner; returning to education to get more letters after your name (or immersing yourself in a subject purely for the sake of learning); or even going back to work – paid or unpaid - retirement in the 21st century is a gift.

You might be thinking "That's all well and good Larry but these things require money, and that's one thing I don't have!" To those people I say: that's a fascinating story, ever thought about adapting it for the stage? The evidence shows that money plays a far less significant role in our overall happiness than you would expect, and if you gauge your success, status or happiness on how much you have in the bank then you're in for a rude awakening.

If you concentrate instead on reviving your sex-life, getting back into dating if you're single, getting to the bottom of your partner's snoring that has been threatening to blow away your marriage, embracing the online superhighway and watching your grandkids opening their birthday presents from the other side of the world; this will make your retirement a thoroughly rewarding phase rather than the detritus that it can be if you roll over and admit defeat.

CHAPTER 9

THE PRICE OF HAPPINESS

They don't call them your 'golden years' because of the fortune that you're likely to have amassed by the time you reach retirement. Although it is hardly a revelation that not having enough money will make most people miserable, having bucket-loads is no guarantee of happiness either. Money has the power to make you miserable if you let it.

> **"Money can't buy happiness, but neither can poverty."** –
> *Leo Rosten*

Studies show that a person's day-to-day happiness increases in line with their income up to approximately £50,000 ($80,000), after which it plateaus. The message is clear: although money can't buy you love, it can buy you happiness up to a point after which you'll need to rely on something else to put a smile on your face. That's where sex comes in! It never gets boring, makes you happy, helps you live longer and, best of all, usually doesn't cost a penny.

A 2004 study published by the National Bureau of Economic Research found that increasing the number of sexual encounters from once a month to once a week boosts a person's happiness by as much as a $50,000 (£31,000) pay rise! So forget about going to the bank first thing in the morning and head to the bedroom (or just stay in the bedroom if you're already there).

As we have established that a certain amount of money does make you happy, it would be disingenuous of me not to devote a certain number of pages to financial matters – particularly focusing on how money matters affected the emotional, relationships and sex-lives of the retirees that I encountered.

Taking a time-out

Suzanne and her late husband Lenny lived in a large town house for over thirty years. Her three children had long since grown up and flown the nest and Lenny passed away after suffering a major stroke. Suzanne was a shrewd business woman, managing the family business – a small car insurance firm. Shortly after Lenny's funeral, Suzanne made the tough decision to sell, unable to cope with the grief and commit to the long hours required to keep the company afloat.

A fortnight after the sale of her business, Suzanne's daughter Lucy appeared on the doorstep with an armful of estate agents' brochures. Suzanne was still fragile but agreed that downsizing seemed the only sensible option. Although I am not implying that Suzanne was coerced into moving, I think it's fair to say that she wasn't in the right frame of mind to be making such a life-changing decision – and she agreed. After living in the flat for four years, Suzanne was sick of feeling boxed in and regretted the move. The problem was that house prices skyrocketed in the meantime, and her options had been severely restricted.

It's always best to take a time-out and wait until the initial shock that follows such a tragic event to pass. The lesson here, for once, is: do nothing - give yourself time to heal.

BEWARE: A common trap people fall into when they make a snap decision on property and decide to downsize is to sell any surplus furniture and possessions. Remember that any move back up the property ladder has to bear the brunt of this additional cost.

REMEMBER...

+ The loss of a partner can impair your judgment at a time when you may need to make some difficult decisions. Although money may not top your list of priorities at this point, you could be entitled to claim up to 100% of a late partner's state pension, in addition to national insurance contributions.

+ Retirement is a significant life-event, step back and focus on the positive. Take ten minutes to list the things you are thankful for; ask your partner to do the same, and then swap them to remind yourself of the things that you might otherwise take for granted.

+ Life rarely goes to plan. Instead of pining for what might have been, dust yourself off and make a new plan – choose to be happy, healthy, attractive and loved.

Dynamic divorcees

"Have you heard the news Larry? Maurice and Marion are getting a divorce" John says in his funereal voice. He did have an unnerving habit of being right in his grim forecasts. I immediately phoned their eldest son, David, who confirmed the news yet sounded oddly unconcerned. I told him about the research for this book and said I would be interested to know how retirement had contributed to the break-up - he suggested that I go and talk to them myself.

For a recently divorced couple, the Adlers seemed perfectly happy sitting in the same room speaking to me - it must have been the most amicable divorce in history. Maurice clicked into story-telling mode straightaway:

"When you were growing up," he reminisces, "we were fairly well off. We had a large house, nice cars and always took a couple of vacations a year. Marion's sister used to work in Mauritius so we would usually stay with her, or rent a villa for a couple of weeks nearby.

"We planned on selling up and renting an apartment as soon as the boys had moved away, to free up some capital, so that's what we did. We weren't thinking about the future, we just kept on spending."

"In the early years after selling the business, everything was fine. For three years we spent most of our summers on cruises or visiting family in New Jersey.

"Five years ago we realized our money was fast running out and neither of us had ever bothered with a private pension, assuming we'd have enough capital left over to last us. Some years it yielded up to 8 percent interest, now we were down in the low single figures. We knew what had to be done but neither of us wanted to admit it. It was time to sell the house."

"We didn't want to make the same mistake again and couldn't find a suitable rental property - it's cozy and we're both happy here – right Marion?"

"Happy enough" she replied.

I had to ask: "So why the divorce?"

"It's very simple Larry. Marriage was just too damn expensive for us."

It turned out that two single people drawing a pension were better off than a married couple getting by on the joint pension. Because the new house had swallowed up most of their capital, Maurice and Marion had to watch every penny. It was sad to think that this committed couple had felt compelled to end their marriage for purely financial reasons.

+ When planning your finances don't forget to take inflation into account. Even if it averages only four percent a year, in ten years the spending power of an annual income of $18,000 (after tax) would have dropped to a little over $11,500.

+ Make sure you have exhausted all other avenues before selling your house; it is an appreciating asset, even if the housing market is volatile.

+ Consider purchasing an annuity indexed against future inflation. It may give a smaller sum when you retire, but it will provide additional income in later life - when you need it most.

During my research I interviewed a number of couples who took a more creative approach to securing their financial future. These people combined boosting their income with enriching their social life; widening their cultural knowledge, and enjoying more quality time with their partner.

A creative couple

Retirement came as a financial blow to Chris and Celia. His years of working as a environmental officer for a government agency qualified him for the maximum percentage of his salary as pension, but he was shocked to discover that the days of overtime he had put in over the years would not count towards his final pension entitlement.

BEWARE: Although employees in the US are 'employed at will' and don't have to comply with this lengthy legalese, contracts of employment in the UK can be intentionally convoluted (not to mention unbelievably boring). As a general rule: If in doubt, ask your employer well in advance.

Thankfully, Celia had always been a numbers bod, and put together a simple spreadsheet to lay out their finances in black and white, including the following elements:

Household income	Savings	Outgoings	Projected Costs	Wish-list
Salary Pensions Annuities	Current account Savings accounts Bonds Stocks and Shares ISAs etc.	Mortgage payments Utility bills Food Car payments DIY Treats	Week in France Fix boiler (on its last legs) Rachel's wedding	New Laptop House in the Hamptons Luxury cruise

REMEMBER: When jotting down your own household finances remember that it's always better to over-estimate any costs to avoid being caught short.

After balancing these considerations, Chris and Celia could see how much extra income they would need to bring in to meet their outgoings, budget projected costs and tick off items on their 'wish-list'. A close friend who worked in the admissions department of a nearby university mentioned a room-letting scheme being advertised on campus. Chris and Celia agreed it would be a great way of keeping their household income ticking over, as well as the perfect time to try something new.

"One of the most attractive things about taking in foreign students rather than professionals is that they go back to their own homes at the end of each semester", Celia says, "and we can put the extra money toward our own little breaks."

The couple took in one student for three months during the summer and another during the Christmas break.

"It wouldn't suit everyone." Celia says. "We were both a little nervous initially. One of the girls that stayed with us was a lovely Chinese student studying Music. She taught me to cook traditional Chinese dumplings and even did the shopping sometimes – it was a cultural experience as much as anything else. I appreciate that we might have been particularly fortunate, but I have recommended the scheme to friends in a similar position to Chris and I."

The success of your own experience will ultimately depend on the suitability of the person moving in, so make sure you consider the following before reaching a decision:

+ Have a selection process in place: male/female, age, smoker/ non-smoker etc.

+ Draw up some house rules: how much will they have to chip in for utility bills? Does that include groceries? What is your policy on firearms?

+ Start off with a short-let of three months as a taster then if you realize it's not for you then you won't have to put up with them for too long.

+ Don't be afraid to say 'no' to the first person that looks around the house, especially if they don't take their shoes off at the door, reek of stale whiskey or try to steal your family heirlooms while you're showing them around – you don't want your good manners costing you.

If the idea of taking in a student doesn't grab you, why not consider a young professional? Although you may not have the advantage of knowing when they will be on vacation in advance, professionals will also contribute towards council tax and are not as likely to live a nocturnal existence, only coming out at night to raid your fridge.

REMEMBER: Fewer younger people can afford to get onto the property ladder and must consider rental opportunities instead. This means you can afford to be picky.

If you're still not convinced, then how about living in somebody else's home while they look after your house for a couple of weeks. Home swapping is big business and another creative source of income that this enterprising couple took full advantage of – Alvin Hall eat your heart out!

Home away from home

With many of us now tightening our purse-strings, non-essential purchases such as vacations, new cars, gold-plated toilets and champagne breakfasts have all fallen victim to the first wave of cutbacks. It is therefore no surprise that home swapping is becoming an increasingly popular alternative to forking out on fancy vacations that often fall well short of the glossy photos in the brochure.

A recent survey commissioned by Lloyds TSB Insurance found that around 1.6 million people in the UK are on course to arrange a house swap in 2011 – more than twice the previous year's total.

Home swapping, as the name implies, is the relatively modern phenomenon of temporarily swapping your home with someone in another part of the world – allowing you to travel globally for a fraction of the cost of a normal vacation. Spain and Italy are the most popular destinations, closely followed by France. Homeexchange.com includes more than 39,000 listings in 138 countries and emphasizes the kookiness of such schemes, citing examples such as an eccentric home swapper trading his house for a 40-foot yacht, and another adventurous couple trading their villa in Italy for an RV in Oregon to live out their dream of touring the US.

The financial savings you will achieve through home swapping means that you can enjoy more romantic time with your partner, explore unfamiliar places and ultimately, rekindle that dormant passion. What could be more romantic than touring the US in an RV, or eating al fresco at a traditional Italian bistro – think *Lady and the Tramp*.

All you need to do is join a reputable online agency, take some pictures of your home (or yacht) and away you go! As always, there are a few things to bear in mind:

Many sites have small, one-off joining fees after which you can enjoy as many home swaps as you like.

Agencies do not typically accept liability for theft or damage so make sure you are covered. It is recommended that you lock valuables in a designated room if possible, and keep smaller items such as jewellery in an extra safe place, such as a safe.

Another hidden benefit of home swapping is forming lasting friendships with people from all over the world. Reputable sites often have online forums where members can get to know each other a little bit and exchange pictures of their respective homes prior to the swap. You can take the time to get to know the people you are considering swapping with, find out more about their home town and local amenities, and make the most of your vacation.

REMEMBER!

+ Make your finances visible. Create a simple spreadsheet to show your total income, total expenditure and projected spending, including your 'wish-list'.

+ Track your spending over a month to see how much you spend and where your money is really going – you might be surprised.

+ Discuss things openly with the children - you generate more ideas when you work together as a family and they won't be afraid to give you honest feedback!

+ Be brave and use your imagination. Some options may not instantly appeal but you learn a lot more when you are out of your comfort zone – consider the non-financial benefits as well – after all, these are the things that make you happiest.

+ The anxiety that accompanies the run up to retirement can make you reflect on how your assets can be fairly divided among your nearest and dearest (and kept well away from the cold taloned fingers of those money-grubbing in-laws). Death is a natural fear, particularly as we age, but considering my own demise was far less intimidating than what awaited me at Daphne Mauret's dimly-lit apartment...

Facing my fears...

My greatest fear in the whole world isn't spiders, snakes or even ending up in an old people's home after my children finally wash their hands of me: it's housecats. Normal, fluffy, universally adored housecats. I know it's irrational, and slightly odd, but they make my skin crawl. It was clear that Daphne didn't share my phobia.

❝A wise man should have money in his head, but not in his heart.❞ – *Jonathan Swift*

164

When the first wretched thing flew down from the bookshelf and landed in front of me I screamed; Moggy number two sensed my fear, rubbing itself up against my legs, arching its back and squinting at me with malice in its eyes. I jumped back, tripped over the coffee table and knocked an expensive-looking vase onto the floor. I don't know whether it was jumping onto the sofa that gave it away, or the screaming, but Daphne sensed my discomfort and quarantined the beasts in her bedroom.

Daphne's father had built up a large property portfolio which she inherited. After a whirlwind romance in her mid-twenties, Daphne married a young inventor called Tom, but the relationship broke down three years later after she discovered that he was also inventive with the truth. It seemed as if there had been mistakes on both sides but she didn't want to go into the specifics, and I didn't want to pry too much in case she released the cats.

Although the marriage was a disaster, they had a son called Geoffrey who had always advised her with any legal matters, particularly those pertaining to her estate. Part of his counsel included transferring a considerable proportion of her wealth over to him to avoid inheritance tax; it seemed like smart thinking.

"He insisted on having a formal quarterly meeting", Daphne said. "I usually find anything involving money unbearably tedious, but I took such pleasure in watching him go through everything. After the business matters were taken care of we would go to a lovely Italian place for lunch and he'd tell me all about how my grandson - that was, before the accident."

Daphne's son was killed in a car-crash after being unable to avoid colliding with a drunk driver who had swerved onto the wrong side of the road and rammed their car into a ditch.

"Unfortunately, my son had not been so shrewd after all" Daphne says. "He had not yet amended his will to make any provision for me and his wife, an awful woman, inherited everything.

"Couldn't you have contested the will?" I asked.

"Geoffrey was my only son. At the time of his death I could barely drag myself out of bed, let alone get into all of that. Eventually I had to move from my beautiful flat but I was lucky enough to find this place. With rent subsidies and a pension I get by."

Daphne's story was tragic, in terms of having to deal with the unimaginable grief of losing a child, but also because of the difficult, yet completely avoidable financial situation in which she found herself. Although I am terrified of cats, I think the idea that your estate could be divided according to the state rather than according to your own wishes is truly frightening.

REMEMBER!

+ Take Scrooge-like care when passing your wealth to your children. It's understandable that you don't want to be stung by inheritance tax, but ensure the relevant legal safeguards are in place.

+ Try to remain friends with your children's partners. Family feuds are poisonous, dangerous and expensive.

+ Always seek impartial advice. Sometimes even the bank manager can be an ally if you catch them in a good mood.

+ Remember that life is for living. Leave room in your budget for enjoying yourself, otherwise what's the point?

+ Don't let money drive a wedge between you and your loved ones - personal relationships are far more precious than pounds.

Will and last testament:

A leading consumer watchdog estimated that 60% of people die without making a will. Let's face it, nobody likes thinking about their own death (or talking to lawyers), but without a trained pair of eyes making sure you have jumped through the relevant legal hoops, your assets will be divided according to state or federal law rather than your own wishes.

One of the other great things about making a will is all the fun you can you have. Why not insert a couple of unusual conditions? You may as well leave them laughing. Try these for inspiration:

Celebrity jokers:

+ Napoleon Bonaparte specified that he wanted his head shaved and for his locks to be divided equally among his friends. I'm not sure I'll have enough to go around.

+ The author of Treasure Island, Robert Louis Stevenson, tried to leave his birthday to a friend who complained that being born at Christmas meant she never got enough presents.

For the children

+ In 1862 a man called Henry Budd left £200,000 ($325,000) in a trust for his two sons on the condition that neither of them ever grew a moustache.

+ Edith S of Walsall left £50,000 ($80,000), to each of her three children with the proviso that it should not be squandered on "slow horses and fast women and only a very small amount on booze."

Pampered pets:

+ If Forbes magazine produced a rich list for animals then the top-dog would be German Shepherd, Gunther IV, who inherited £92 million ($150 million) from an eccentric German countess in 2000.

+ Last, and definitely my least favorite, is Jonathan Jackson of Columbus, Ohio who dedicated his estate to the creation of a cat house which reportedly came complete with custom-made bedrooms, a gym, a dining hall and a music room.

Having the final word:

+ Anthony Scott included the following sharp-tongued sentiment in his will: 'To my first wife Sue, whom I always promised to mention in my will. Hello Sue!'

The price of a will can vary greatly, but there are many deals to be found on the internet, including '2 for 1' offers for you and your partner. Look out for charity-led schemes which offer the opportunity to make a will for a discounted fee – the proceeds of which are then fed back into the charity.

Dos and Don'ts

Do

+ Use your money to enjoy every day to the full. Spend your money on things that make you feel sexy. Buy some new clothes, go for a massage.

+ Spoil your partner and remember this doesn't have to cost the Earth: leave romantic notes around the house or pen a cheesy poem; book a romantic weekend away; cook a three course meal (without burning the house down). Small gestures make a big difference and spontaneity will bring you closer together and rekindle your sex-life.

+ Above all, remember that you are in charge of your money, not the other way around; if it isn't making you happy then look for happiness elsewhere.

Don't

+ Trade in your sports car for a clapped out banger unless you really have to.

+ Be needlessly stingy. You've worked hard your whole life; take the time to enjoy yourself.

+ Brandish your free bus pass like a badge of honor, it isn't a good look.

+ Feel guilty about blowing the kids' inheritance — it's your money and they should want to see you happy in your sixties, seventies and beyond.

+ Put off making a will - make sure you are the person that decides how your assets will be divided, after all, they were yours.

+ Ignore this list of don'ts.

Happy as Larry

Above all, money should never be considered as an 'end' in itself. This attitude only leads to misery, regardless of your lot. Unfortunately, some financial planning is unavoidable in helping you to build your perfect retirement picture. But the income that you need in order to be happy in retirement is far less than is commonly assumed; far more important is working out how the money that you do have can help you to become a more caring and considerate partner.

Frequent, affectionate gestures show your loved one that their happiness and their needs remain your primary concern. Concentrate on how you can draw on your experience to enjoy a deeper level of intimacy than ever before.

As the Little Prince, Abraham Maslow and Kofi Annan would all testify (probably): we need to feel valued, to belong to a 'community' and to form meaningful relationships and watch them grow – this is the real secret to happiness in retirement.

But it's easier said than done. If the thought of taking a chance and forming new friendships or finding romance makes you feel queasy, it might be time to think about putting yourself back out there. In the modern age, there's only one place to start the search: the internet.

CHAPTER 10

CYBER RETIREMENT-COMMUNITIES

When I first started writing this book, nearly 13 years ago, the world was a simple place where words ruled over acronyms, twitter was the sound a bird made (or the behaviour of a twit) and computers were ugly grey blocks of plastic that responded obediently when prodded. Those days are gone. The machines have conspired against us, underlining our flaws like a sadistic school teacher with an everlasting red pen, and bleeping profanities to dampen our spirit.

> **" The Internet is becoming the town square for the global village of tomorrow."** –
> *Bill Gates*

But the rise of the digital world, namely, the internet, has revolutionized the way we interact and learn. Originating as a mode of remote communication used by the military, the World Wide Web has exploded into a constantly-expanding source of information and a medium through which we can connect with friends and family, and find that special someone. The internet is the great leveller of the 21st century where anybody can express themselves to a global audience – so it's no surprise that there is a lot of crap to sift through as well.

13 years ago I worked from the assumption (largely based on my own computer knowledge) that Baby Boomers were essentially clueless about technology and wrote a glossary of terms, including words like 'email', 'floppy diskette' (yes, I wrote 'diskette') and 'scanner', but you'll be happy to know that I decided to spare you the tedium here.

Number crunching

The World Wide Web Consortium estimated that the total number of people using the internet back in December 1998 was a paltry 147 million (3.6 percent of the world's population) compared with more than two billion people in March 2011.

Despite these statistics, a disproportionately low percentage of Baby Boomers are reaping the benefits. A survey by the Pew Research Center's Internet & American Life Project in 2009 found that although Baby Boomers have started embracing the online world, with 70% of adults aged between 50-64 logging on, this figure drops to 38% in over-65s. This is a serious issue that needs urgent attention, particularly when you consider Eurostat's findings that 63% of the over-65s who did embrace the internet felt that it helped them to connect with family and friends.

Some countries have a more progressive approach with the Home Computing Network in Japan opening more than 300 specialized schools where the average age of students exceeds 60!

At least part of the blame for these lackluster stats should be shouldered by the person who invented the term 'Silver Surfer'. I imagine a group of twenty-somethings brainstorming ideas for a marketing campaign aimed at internet-users in later-life, when somebody shouts 'Senile Surfer!' Everybody laughs before deciding that they might have to tone it down a bit, eventually settling on the more patronizing 'Silver Surfer' which, incidentally, sounds like a geriatric superhero. I'm not a 'Silver Surfer'. I'm an internet-user who doesn't need a fanfare or a gold-star whenever I manage to turn a computer on.

Get connected

I want to (briefly) look at the four main social networking websites that form the main hub of the cyber community that have transformed the way we stay in touch with family and friends, broaden our social convoy across generations and geographical divides, satisfy our basic human need for companionship and allows us to make the most of the freedom that retirement offers.

Facebook:

IN A NUTSHELL: Facebook is the world's largest social networking site with more than 750 million users worldwide.

Create a profile, add your details and invite people to become your Facebook 'friends'. You can then exchange messages with anybody who accepts. Upload your digital photographs and 'tag' them (an electronic nametag assigned to each person in a picture) or view other photo albums in which you are tagged. You will be notified whenever you are tagged in a photoand can just log into your account to see it, or untag yourself and ask them to take it down if it isn't very flattering.

You can use Facebook to keep in touch with people (or send offensive messages to ex-employees) and update your 'wall' (virtual notice board) to tell people what you've been doing. You can search for ex-school friends or colleagues from bygone years; rekindle old friendships; find out for sure if your first major relationship really could have worked out differently (although that might not be such a great idea as we'll see), and arrange to see people without having to lurk in the bushes outside their house. It's very convenient.

If you want to start a book group or meet other aficionados of Byzantine culture then start a Facebook group; if you feel strongly about a political issue and want to start a petition, start a Facebook group. You can be part of something in seconds, and because the network of users is so vast, you will meet people who share your interests, however niche.

REMEMBER: Only post messages or photos that you would be happy to show anybody because once it's 'out there' there's no going back…

Blog

IN A NUTSHELL: A blend of the phrase 'Web Log', your blog is an online journal where you can share highly perceptive observations or inane rants with the world.

Because anybody can set up their own blog for free through popular web sites such as www.blogger.com and www.blogspot.com , quality varies from professional, well-crafted journalism to libel-littered trash-talk. The best part of blogging is accumulating 'visitors' by writing things people want to read and leaving a comment on other blogs in the hope that they reciprocate - referred to as 'link love' in modern parlance. Give and ye shall receive! Blog about what interests you:

- If you have green thumbs start a blog sharing your gardening tips with the world. As your confidence grows you could start posting pictures and instructional videos.

- If you're undertaking a renovation project on an old barn before moving into your perfect retirement home, chart your progress. It may be difficult to attract visitors to begin with so tell your family and friends to drop by and comment.

+ Always wanted to showcase your erotic stories? Start a blog under a pseudonym (probably best not to let your family and friends know about this one).

+ Write recipes, take photographs of your creations, and post them online. Look for other blogs about food and connect with bloggers with similar interests – it could be a recipe for finding love in retirement too.

Twitter

IN A NUTSHELL: A 'micro-blogging' service where you can let people know what you are up to in bite size 140-character 'tweets'.

Tweet to let other people know what you're doing (remember to always 'think before you tweet' – although you can delete messages that you post, things have a nasty habit of resurfacing at a later date). Follow other users' tweets and start an online, interactive conversation. Twitter is often derided as being a forum for triviality, but it isn't only used by people telling you what they had for breakfast or what color socks they're wearing. It can also be used to:

+ Communicate with your friends and family, for free

+ Find people with the same niche interests

+ Promote your blog, attracting more visitors

The site has millions of users, including celebrities such as Barack Obama, Oprah Winfrey and Stephen Fry – referred to collectively as the 'twitterati'. In addition, 'trending' is where many people on twitter are talking about the same subject; looking at what's 'trending' is a great way of getting a snapshot of the stories that have captured the world's imagination.

FACT: The oldest Twitter user was 104-year-old British woman, Ivy Bean, who tweeted her daily activity from her residential home – often professing her fondness for fish and chips and the pop-star, Peter Andre. Sadly, Ivy died in July 2010, but remains an inspiration to us all: you are never too old to go online.

YouTube

IN A NUTSHELL: An online place to watch and share videos.

Showcasing everything from the latest chart toppers to comedy routines, TV programs that you haven't seen for thirty years (somebody somewhere will have uploaded it), or more practical videos offering exercise and diet tips from fellow-retirees and sex advice in later-life – YouTube has everything you could wish to see, and a lot of things you'll wish you hadn't.

But it's not just about watching videos; as the site's tag-line proclaims: "broadcast yourself". If you can play Bohemian Rhapsody on the spoons, or can still do 10 one-arm press-ups at 80 then put it on YouTube! When you sign up you are given your own channel. Start by 'subscribing' to channels you like and interact with other subscribers.

I spoke to many retirees who had either been coerced into the digital world by younger relatives or through involvement in other leisure activities and groups that used the internet to communicate with its members. Eric was skeptical at first but managed to forego his cynicism and soon found social networking a cinch.

Now I'm a believer

Eric worked at Unilever screwing the tops on bottles on washing detergent. The company announced that they were relocating the factory to China to cut labor costs which meant job cuts through the region. Eric was one of the lucky ones. They offered a redundancy package which would see his company pension equaling the maximum state pension even though he had yet to qualify for his full entitlement, or the opportunity to retrain for a computerized customer-service role. He chose redundancy.

"I've never been much of a techie," Eric says, "I didn't fancy having to learn all this computer-stuff at my age. And to be honest, I just didn't really want to work anymore.

"My daughter, Alison, works in the civil service and married an Australian sports journalist. They split their time between Perth and Preston now. I was sorry to see her go, but she suggested we used the internet to keep in touch."

"My mobile contract is with Orange and they offered the cheapest internet deal to existing customers. I looked into it, gave them a call and they told me I needed a router to direct the signal to my computer. You just plug it in and away you go."

Eric signed up for a free email address and began exchanging emails with his daughter, Alison, every few days. She took pictures of their new house; of their dog, Dexter; and pictures of his granddaughter, Daisy, just hours after the birth – but this was only the beginning.

"It's like anything" Eric says, "the more you learn, the better you get. Alison told me about Skype, a great program which lets you talk to each other using web cameras - and it's free. It beats having to spend a fortune on phone calls and I like being able to watch my granddaughter grow up properly, instead of only seeing each other once a year which is all I could afford. I sometimes read her bedtime stories and it works surprisingly well because of the time difference."

As well as staying in touch with your family, tracing your ancestors has become an internet phenomenon in recent years and carries the advantage that your great, great, great, great (and so on) grandmother from the 17th Century won't be phoning you every five minutes once you've tracked her down: genealogy could be the missing piece of your perfect retirement picture!

Tracing your family tree

The site 'Genes Reunited', (sister site of the social networking site Friends Reunited), enables you to search through various online databases including national census information, marriage certificate databases, death certificates etc. -create and edit a family tree online so that you can build a clearer picture of where you came and find out whether your descendents were landed gentry or petty criminals.

REMEMBER: If researching your family tree floats your boat, consider the internet as a starting-point and only take information that you uncover as a guide before you have definitive proof (official documents or verified first-hand accounts etc.). Remember to watch out for scams. Anybody claiming to be a long-lost relative before asking how much your house is worth should be treated with caution.

The darker side of the digital age...

With each leap in technology comes a renewed risk of temptation. We are continually exposed to hazards that can threaten even the sturdiest of relationships. The digital world doesn't change the way we behave it just gives us more technologically-advanced ways to screw up.

One retiree told me about his ex-wife who had joined Friends Reunited. This first generation social networking site lets you search for old friends or colleagues from around the world and get back in touch. Naomi was born in England, and emigrated to America with her parents shortly after leaving school; the opportunity to reconnect with her past was hugely appealing.

After checking her inbox that morning Naomi saw a message from her first serious boyfriend back in her late-teens. They exchanged a series of emails updating each other on the paths their lives had taken, and Oliver quickly became her confidant.

Several months later, Oliver announced that he would be in America on a business trip and asked if she wanted to meet. She knew that his marriage had recently broken down, and they had been barely disguising their flirting for weeks, but she disregarded the insinuations in his offer and told herself that they would just meet up and have dinner. That weekend turned out to be the start of their affair - and the end of her 30-year marriage.

I don't want to sound like a Grinch but the notion of getting back in touch with old flames is often built on little more than idealized memories and bad Hollywood movies. Remember that you broke up for a reason, and if you put yourself back in the mindset you were in when the relationship broke down, you might not be so keen to revive it.

BEWARE: Rekindling that first love is often just a harmful fairytale myth that has the power to leave long-standing relationships in tatters.

Although Friends Reunited does not explicitly condone this behavior, more modern websites like www.ashleymadison.com have caused controversy by positioning themselves as online forums for adultery. Their tag-line: "Life is short. Have an affair" is fairly unabashed and unambiguous. The direct approach does seem to be popular though with the site now boasting more than 10 million members around the world.

Technology has no moral conscience. It is neither 'good' nor 'bad' but offers massive benefits for those who choose to see them, and opportunities to make some pretty terrible decisions, if you're looking for trouble. There is no doubt that during retirement, a time where you are anxious about losing touch with a network of colleagues and feel isolated, the internet can be used to solidify relationships and establish new ties.

It might be difficult to dump your cynicism, or the stubborn mindset that you are content as you are, which is too often a smokescreen masking a fear of rejection (I learnt that in 'Armchair Psychology 101'), but embracing the present and replacing your doubts with a willingness to learn from new experiences can be extremely rewarding as you enter the next phase – so what's stopping you?

The unexpected twists and turns of life tend to come in more rapid succession as we age. Retirement can lay bare some home truths about our personal happiness and our relationships, precipitating the realization that it is time to do something differently. If you are single, dating can lead to purely plutonic relationship, companionship and intimacy: whether it's a shopping partner or a more satisfying sex-life that you're after.

CHAPTER 11

DATING and THE DIGITAL AGE

Singledom is increasingly prevalent among Baby Boomers where the divorce rate is soaring faster than a banker's blood pressure. But there are a few undeniable perks of single-life, namely: freedom, peace and quiet, financial savings and not having to worry about your partner no longer finding you attractive. Many retirees who found love in later-life told me they felt stunted by a fear of failure or an inability to let go of the emotional baggage from a previous relationship.

> **"Dating is pressure and tension. What is a date, really, but a job interview that lasts all night?"** –
> *Jerry Seinfeld*

If your relationship ended shortly after hitting retirement, or you have been affected by the loss of a spouse, you will need time to heal; exactly how long is entirely down to you. You may have friends trying to 'help' by trying to set you up with friends or encouraging you to meet new people – but don't rush yourself, wait until you are ready. In the wise words of modern sage and lead-singer of The Supremes, Diana Ross: "you can't hurry love/ no, you just have to wait."

My wife first knew me as young and skinny Larry moving into slightly older fatter Larry right through to jobless fat Larry and now – I might add – a slightly thinner Larry, with a mysteriously thicker head of hair. The journey you take together as a couple means that you let your defences down gradually over the years. It is natural to feel vulnerable both physically and emotionally after deciding to get back into dating. There is no shame in admitting this to yourself, or to your date; just don't make it the sole subject of conversation otherwise you won't have to worry about things going any further.

One woman I know pulled down her blouse and said "if you can stand this then fine" – an unconventional, risqué and somewhat disturbing tactic, but it got things off to a flying start as you might expect. They ended up dating for a couple of months – not that I'm advocating flashing as an acceptable way to attract a prospective partner. Just don't rule it out.

Dump the baggage

REMEMBER: Although memories make you who you are, your past shouldn't define your attitude in the present - don't let guilt or fear get in the way of your future happiness!

You may have been married for decades and found your relationship reaching its natural end-point; or perhaps you discovered your partner at one of her 'book club' meetings and wondered when it has ever been necessary to physically re-enact *Lady Chatterley's Lover* over a butcher's block with your next-door neighbour. The point is trust issues can affect your ability to trust in the future. Take the positive experiences with you and leave the negative behind.

> **" Sometimes you put walls up not to keep people out, but to see who cares enough to break them down. " –**
>
> *Anona*

There are a few common anxieties which deter many retirees from reconnecting with their sexuality and maximising their happiness in retirement:

+ **Children sceptical of your renewed interest in finding love**
  Whether your children's concerns are well-intentioned or driven by self-interest is irrelevant – this is your retirement; you do not have to slow down or apologise for seeking companionship or great sex at any age.

+ **General insecurity over the question 'am I over the hill?'**
  Dating website eHarmony recently revealed that over 55s were the fastest-growing demographic joining their dating site. You can find love, friendship or casual sex at any age.

+ **Loss of confidence in appearance or chronic health problems**
  If you have been with the same partner for thirty years and find yourself back on the market it's easy to lose confidence in your appearance. Re-building your self-esteem can be daunting. If you have health problems you're not alone. People should be able to accept you as you are; if they can't then you're better off without them.

+ **Fear of rejection**
  With stepping out of your comfort zone comes learning and with risk comes reward. Fear will only hold you back; repeat your affirmations, return to the pledge and jump in at the deep-end – if you are faced with rejection then draw a line under it and move on. Everybody has to deal with rejection at some point; it's how you deal with this rejection that counts.

For the majority of people, sharing life experiences and physical intimacy is an integral aspect of their personal wellbeing. With this in mind here's some encouraging news for both sexes

Women: Because you live longer than men on average, you can afford to take your time in considering your options – if you aren't interested in finding love then that's fine.

Men: Ok, we might die sooner, but every cloud has a silver-lining. What better incentive for staying healthy? The longer you can hold out, the thinner the competition. A 2009 report commissioned by the AARP (American Association of Retired Persons) found that by the age of 50 women outnumber men by 954 to 920 per 1000 births, and at 65 that changes to 871 women for just 791 men – I like those numbers…

So, there are millions of retirees just like you floundering around just waiting to meet Mr or Mrs Right. There's only so much floundering you can do until you say enough is enough and decide to take some affirmative action. But where is your dream partner hiding? The digitisation of the dating landscape may have changed the way a lot of us look for love in the 21st Century, but some of the old classics are just as effective today as they ever were.

Introduction agencies

Introduction agencies are the respectable red-brick institutions of the dating world. They like to use words like 'traditional', 'professional' and 'dependable' to differentiate themselves from dating websites which they denounce as love lotteries with more chance of being scammed out of your savings than finding that special someone.

An introduction agency is still worth considering if:

+ Money is not an option. Words like 'traditional', 'professional' and 'dependable' are also used to justify the sometimes inordinate cost of such agencies.

- You want a more personal, tailored service. Agencies invest their time in finding suitable partners based on information that they gather through face-to-face interviews with every client.

- You are worried about security or just don't have the time. A trained member of staff will create your dating profile for you and, even if you are very self-aware and honest, it can be difficult to sum yourself up (truthfully) in a few sentences.

- You are concerned about anonymity. Whereas with online dating strangers will often be able to see at least a preview of your profile, introductory agencies ensure the confidentiality of their clientele, with more exclusive (expensive) agencies making their employees sign confidentiality agreements.

In our society of great expectations and quick-fixes, from fast food to Botox, we all want results and we want them ten minutes ago. No longer content with placing classified ads in the backs of newspapers and sending a letter to a PO Box address to express your interest in a prospective partner, even 'regular' dating has been unable to dodge this trend of turbo-charging every facet of our lives: enter speed dating.

Speed dating

Arguably somewhat brutal, speed dating involves a bunch of people of a similar age meeting at a designated place, paying a small fee and spending a minute or two with each participant before changing places in a round-robin format and ticking boxes afterwards to indicate who they would like to see again.

Think of it as a cross between the Mad Hatter's tea party and Charles Darwin's 'survival of the fittest' principle compressed into two hours of potential rejection and misery. Unless you are confident that you can encapsulate your personality into a few snappy sound bites then speed-dating might not be for you. It can however be an enjoyable social activity with friends if taken with a sizeable pinch of salt.

Besides, there's always the advantage that if you make a huge faux pas, you are more than likely to be saved by the bell – and how much can you embarrass yourself in a minute? That's right, quite a lot.

Dating sites

Dating sites cater for all regardless of age, background, sexual orientation or predilection. Looking for marriage material? Try eHarmony; more interested in meeting a millionaire then finding love - who am I to take the moral high ground? Try sugardaddie.com; so you're an orthodox Jew? JDate is the site for you etc.

Although there are senior-specific sites such as Fiftyalready.com, Justseniorsingles.com and www.seniormatch.com, many of the larger 'general' sites have broad user-bases from all age-groups so we'll focus on those instead.

Although I am a blissfully happy married man, I wanted to sign up to a few dating sites myself to see what features were on offer and do some brief comparisons in the name of research on your behalf... for more reviews go to www.reviewcenter.com which features 'star' reviews and comments from thousands of internet-users from around the world.

Match.com

Registration is free and includes a number of basic functions such as being able to send a 'wink' to show your interest in another user – there isn't a cyber equivalent for 'light slap on the behind' which was disappointing. You will need an email address to register - visit hotmail or yahoo to sign-up for free if you haven't got one.

You will be asked to enter your personal details including your relationships status, personality type, smoker or non-smoker, occupation, lifestyle interests and a photo. Features include instant messaging, which takes place in an online chat room like setting, and users can create quizzes for other prospective dates to assess their compatibility.

If you are somebody that thinks they know exactly what they are looking for, but always ends up with the polar opposite, then perhaps eHarmony is more up your street...

eHarmony

eHarmony matches you up with compatible people automatically after taking you through a 'Relationship Questionnaire' including 29 categories spanning your values, character, intellect and sense of humour – and they must be doing something right as the site is reputedly responsible for an average of 542 people getting married everyday in the US alone, although it doesn't mention how many of them get divorced six months later.

I completed this questionnaire (in the name of research) and after half an hour of non-stop questions a screen popped up stating that, unfortunately, their computers could not find any suitable matches for me – not one. I can imagine that for someone actually looking for love, the idea of being knocked back by millions of people at the same time, isn't exactly the self-confidence boost that they need. Thanks eHarmony.

OkCupid

Another popular choice with 1.3 million visitors in February 2011 - although perhaps Valentine's day might go some way to explaining the spike in web traffic. One of my favourite features on offer was the facility to create your own blog (see below for more on this), send instant messages to people you like and join forums where you can interact with other users or start your own 'thread' to pique a potential partner's interest.

OkCupid finds suitable matches through running a complex algorithm from data gathered by asking you a number of questions, recording your answer, the answer you would expect from a potential partner, and how important you deem the question. OkCupid can then pair-up suitable matches and everybody lives happily ever after – that's the idea anyway.

The majority of large dating websites offer tiered membership structures, allowing you to sign up for free and pay a monthly subscription fee to enhance the visibility of your profile, unlock more features – i.e. more efficient ways of filtering your ideal matches and alternative means of communicating with other members.

CAUTION – Watch out for automatically recurring subscription fees on paying sites! These are marketed as an ultra-convenient way for you not to have to worry about how much money is coming out of your account. I would prefer to worry about how much money is coming out of my account and not have any nasty surprises at the end of the month.

Once you have made the leap and signed up a site (or several) the next step is to create a profile which people are powerless to resist.

The perfect profile – 10 golden rules

It can be difficult for most people to describe their positive characteristics, not for me though: I'm intelligent, good looking, hilarious, fabulously successful and surprisingly modest too.

Remember, you are selling yourself here. You need to market yourself effectively and play to your strengths to stand out from the crowd and, as in a job interview, turn any negatives into positives. Follow this dating Decalogue to create the perfect profile:

- **Always include a photograph** – preferably one where you haven't got your eyes closed - and make sure your wife isn't in the background.

- **Be positive** – it's ok to say that you are successful and you must emphasise your strengths, but try not to be too arrogant.

- **Honesty is the best policy** – there's nothing wrong with bending the truth but lying is only advisable if you can get away with it.

- **Don't mention the 'D' word** – even Dolly Parton can't bring herself to say it; although everyone has baggage, you don't need to offload it on somebody you haven't even met yet.

- **Don't play the sympathy card** – don't go into detail about your average Saturday night if it involves weeping into a microwave meal for one while watching Titanic, it isn't sexy.

- **Don't judge** – some people think that writing things like 'must weigh less than 200lb' will filter the number of respondents. It will, to zero.

- **Let your personality shine** – why are you different, what makes you such a great catch? If you can't think of anything, think harder, or elaborate on the truth.

- **Show, don't tell** – if you think you have a GSOH then slip in a few jokes: don't say that you're witty but prove that you're not in the next line.

- **Write, edit, re-write** – make sure there aren't any glaring spelling errors, typos or ambiguities, especially if you're claiming to be intelligent (which you shouldn't be because of the previous rule).

- **Update as you go** – as you become more aware of the kind of people your profile is attracting and tweak it to suit your personal preferences.

If you're finding it too difficult to come up with your own profile or just can't find the motivation then **mysinglefriend.com** might be more up your street. This dating site is designed for people that would 'cringe at the idea of online dating' – which encompasses virtually everybody – cunning. The real selling-point is that you can get a friend to refer you, write your profile and do all the hard work - and don't worry - whatever they write is sent to you first for 'sign off' so you can be sure they really are a friend.

BEWARE - Scammers create convincing fake profiles to manipulate nice people like you. The best way to avoid getting stung is to exercise the same level of caution that you would in the offline world. Don't divulge any personal details; don't give anybody any money; and always report anything suspicious to the site's security team.

You might have a hard time believing this but not everything non-scammers claim on online dating websites turns out to be true either. White lies crop up usually as a reactionary response to a fear of rejection; getting back into dating can be an intimidating experience. You're laying yourself on the line and making yourself vulnerable. According to research by OkTrends (a blog written by ex-Harvard math majors based on the data gathered from users of OkCupid):

- Men and women exaggerate their height by an average of two inches.

+ Both sexes inflate their salary by 20%.

+ Women understate their weight by an average of 20lb.

To avoid disappointment, always assume that everybody else has bent the truth as least as much as you have, and remember to follow a few simple guidelines when arranging that all-important first date:

+ Always meet in a public place, don't agree to visit your date at home (or invite them to yours), and tell a friend where you're going.

+ Make an effort. Don't go straight from the gym or turn up in a string vest - dress nice and your date will appreciate the gesture.

There's nothing wrong with a glass of wine but limit your intake; you may think you're being charming and debonair, but you're not, and you are putting yourself at risk.

If you don't feel comfortable for any reason, or have a Columbo-style hunch that something is awry, then make your excuses and leave – trust your instincts. This isn't an excuse to just leave if your date says something that you don't agree with or slurps the soup, but don't take any chances.

Rules of attraction

MYTH: Mature women are sex-mad cougars prowling for toy-boys

FACT: The evidence flies in the face of salacious popular culture and suggests otherwise.

Regardless of what celebrities like Demi Moore, Madonna and Jordan (yes, I was scraping the barrel there) might get up to, a study of the age preferences of 22,000 online dating users lead by Dr Michael Dunn, a psychologist from the University of Wales, showed that as men age the age-gap between themselves and the women they were attracted to widened; but women typically went for men of a similar age, attracted to the wealth and status that maturity supposedly brings.

This phenomenon is frequently linked to 'evolutionary theory' which says that men are naturally attracted by fertility and women by security and status. Of course, this is just a generalization, but the science seems to back it up, and there's nothing wrong with the occasional generalization.

Retirement as an adventure

Fiona had been divorced for five years after a long and happy marriage to her ex-military man ended amicably. John was discharged from duty after damaging his leg in an IED blast and lived on disability allowance ever since. Fiona worked as a team leader in a local supermarket giving her a chance to regain some energy before returning home.

> **❝❝It is good to have an end to journey towards, but it is the journey that matters in the end."** –
> *Ursula K. Le Guin*

Born in Berlin, Fiona moved between schools as her father, a humourless and overbearingly bright pilot, was continually reassigned, uprooting the family. "It was difficult making new friends and getting into a routine before finding out that we had to move again" she says.

There was another side to the story too as Fiona explained that although it was frustrating, there was a real sense of adventure about living this transitional lifestyle. "You could say that I never had the chance to get bored – things changed that much. As a child, I just found that exciting, and didn't appreciate how difficult it was for my older sister and my mother.

"Then I met John" Fiona says. "I found my rock. but sometimes you don't need a rock weighing you down. It's important to feel free to move and to grow. I missed that freedom and I could feel the frustration building up."

The problem was that they were no longer lovers but more like close friends; mutually dependent on one another for companionship – a familiar story. When she tells him that things have changed there is no big showdown. Fiona moves out while they try and sell the house but still calls around every day for a coffee and to help wherever she can.

Fiona looks through the classified ads in the newspaper but doesn't like that you can't see a picture of your prospective date and only have three or four lines of print on which to base your judgment of a person you are agreeing to meet.

As it happens, John is a keen internet-user, regularly posting messages on military forums or updating his blog of short-stories based on his army experiences and hoping one day to turn them into a book. She has an email address that she occasionally uses to contact her daughter and granddaughter. She searches for 'dating sites' and signs up to a site that asks her to enter a user-name.

❝The past is a guidepost, not a hitching post.❞ – *L. Thomas Holdcroft*

"I went for 'feistyfi62'" she says, "I didn't want people thinking I was looking for anything too serious." Fiona is clear about what she wants and it isn't windy walks or trips to the garden center.

"I went on a couple of dates and I was excited rather than nervous. I had to think about what to wear. I hadn't been on a date in over thirty years. I even practised introducing myself in front of the mirror – I feel ridiculous telling you this – I felt nineteen again!

They met at an Italian restaurant. He was slender and good-looking, a silver-fox in a fitted charcoal suit and polished leather shoes. The conversation flowed and, bar a couple of awkward moments, it was an entertaining evening. She zones out as he speaks, imagining him without the suit; undoing his belt before the dynamic switches and he takes control as John had all those years ago.

"He was very attractive", Fiona says. "But as the night ran on, he became progressively more drunk and instead of kissing him goodnight I had to call him a cab and pay the driver extra to make sure he got home. I didn't see him again. Call me old-fashioned but I don't like to be able to out-drink my dates."

Fiona didn't let her first experience deter her, and became somewhat of a serial dater. She is a modern woman and always insists on 'Going Dutch' (splitting the bill) - the hallmark of good modern dating etiquette.

"The first man I actually had sex with after John was a 45-year-old recent divorcee called Patrick. The world didn't move, as I had hoped it would, but we did see each other for about six months. Our time together served a purpose for both of us – I felt attractive, physically. That contact had been missing for so long and I hadn't realised just how much I had needed it."

Retirement had been a chance for Fiona to take a step back, revaluate what she wanted; commitment didn't really come into it.

"Meeting new people, sharing new experiences and feeling sexy again has transformed my life. It's nice to feel alive from time to time and meeting new, exciting men has put that sense of the unknown back into my life – I love it and my confidence is sky high!"

It doesn't matter whether you join an introduction agency, an online dating site or embrace the world of social networking to meet new people. If you make the choice to take a more proactive attitude to life and realize that you are entitled to be healthy, attractive and loved, this will ultimately lead to happiness in retirement as Elaine's story proved testament to...

A gift worth waiting for...

Elaine was 19 when she met Steven and 19 and a half when they decided to get married. She worked as a legal secretary while Steven studied medicine. Despite both families voicing their concerns over the pace of their relationship, the couple wed and moved in to a small rented apartment - three weeks later Elaine was pregnant.

Baby Elle made her appearance two days after Steven had taken his second-year exams and the following weeks were marred by thoughts of job applications and anxiety over the imminent arrival. Steven took a part-time shelf-stacking job at a local supermarket to support the three of them while Elaine was on maternity leave, struggling to cope with post-natal depression. Elaine blamed herself for ruining her husband's career plans; she dropped Elle off at her parents' house every other weekend to take a break from the screaming and the constant nappy-changing.

She struggles up the two flights of stairs with armfuls of shopping, pushes the door open and sees discarded clothes strewn across the floor in front of her, following the trail up to her panting husband on top of a petit blonde. She drops the bags as he jumps up, arms outstretched as the blonde pulls the cover up to conceal herself. The scene is vivid even now.

"I was devastated" Elaine says. "He broke my heart. When I look back I can see that we weren't in the same place –I know it wasn't my fault but I was naive to think we could play happy families; he wasn't ready to commit, let alone handle the responsibility of taking care of a child.

"Steven made all kinds of promises about maintaining contact with Elle that came to nothing – the maintenance checks still arrived but he stopped visiting as regularly and by the time Elle was five it was down to birthday and Christmas cards. I eventually told him that his input was more disruptive than anything else - it wasn't fair - and he had to commit to regular contact or cut it entirely.

"He made his choice and the contact stopped. When Elle was 16 I told her about her dad; where she could find him and what happened. She eventually decided to make contact. He's married to the same woman that he had been seeing behind my back and they have their own family. The last thing I heard, he was the clinical director of an inner-city hospital. Elle still talks to him sometimes I think – I'm glad she feels able to do that."

Elaine was obviously a deeply caring woman; a doting mother and grandmother. When I met her she was still working part-time as a nursery nurse at a primary school just outside Leeds. Elle was 34 and married with a daughter of her own.

"I couldn't move on after Steven, not completely" she says. "I'm not bitter, I don't think, I just lost interest in men. It became a running joke in the family that I was destined to be an old spinster."

On Elaine's 60th birthday she has a big party at her house to celebrate, inviting all of the family and plenty of close friends to mark the occasion.

"I got all the usual gifts; bath salts, perfume, little ornaments, a senior joke book – the usual tat. The most unexpected present was from Elle - a year's subscription to an introduction agency. I was mortified at first but agreed to give it a try, not so much out of a sense of wanting to actually find anybody, but I couldn't bear to think of all that money going to waste."

Elaine went along to the agency and had to have an informal interview with a 'matching consultant' who asked her lots of questions about career, her interests, likes and dislikes and what she was looking for in a partner.

"It was as embarrassing as you would expect" Elaine says. "The woman that took me through the process was very helpful though, and suggested a couple of matches straightaway and showed me their photos. I felt callous dismissing people based on a brief description and a photograph but that's just the process."

Three days later Elaine got a call from her matching consultant to tell her that a 58-year-old gentleman had just been into the agency who she thought would be a great match. She sent his profile to Elaine's email address and when it finally came through she was immediately attracted to him, noticed that they had many mutual interests including classical music, skiing and crosswords and agreed to meet.

"It was the first time I had been on a date in nearly 15 years" Elaine says. "I could feel the butterflies in my stomach as the taxi pulled up outside the restaurant. I walked into the room and knew there was no backing out; I tried to look as inconspicuous as possible but I was sure everyone could tell that I was on a date – then I spotted the suave stranger from the photograph."

"He was lovely - tanned with thick auburn hair brushed into a casual side-parting" she says. "He said all the right things too but there was no chemistry. We did arrange to see each other again though, and I'm so glad we did…"

The next time they met the conversation shifted to music and Elaine mentioned that she used to play the piano as a schoolgirl and Jeremy said he had been taking lessons for some time and was preparing for his Grade 3 exam.

"I had considered getting lessons again; particularly now I was retired and didn't have the excuse of being too busy." Elaine says. "Jeremy kindly gave me the number of his teacher who lived close by and I rang him the next day. The first couple of lessons reminded me of why I stopped in the first place; I had no talent for music whatsoever – I was awful – but it wasn't a dead loss, the teacher had been widowed for five years and when I told him that that would be my last lesson he asked if I would like to go to the theatre with him – that was five years ago and he proposed in January."

After 30 years of single-life Elaine finally found love. It might not have been through the Introduction Agency directly, but finding the confidence to join up (in this case, spurred on slightly by her determined family) renewed her interest in finding love and opened up possibilities in retirement. As far as I know, Elaine is now living with her piano man and has finally been able to put the past behind her.

CHAPTER 12

MAKING THE MOST OF NOW

THE happiest retirees I met all had something in common (aside from having retired): their lifestyles flew in the face of the idea that once you hit a certain age you should expect to lose mental and physical functioning and wave goodbye to a great sex-life.

From June and Allen at the beginning of my journey to Fiona the internet dater and Jack and Edna Jones (the couple with near-blinding smiles and matching sportswear) who were self-assured in the belief that they were entitled to feel happy, healthy, attractive and loved. This positivity radiated in the way they looked, their zest for life and the enduring strength of their relationships.

These people didn't allow regrets, previous hardship, or the obstacles that they encountered to hold them back and burden their future. They didn't focus on 'retirement' as a daunting phase in their lives. Instead they took the culmination of experiences and built on them, growing together and embracing a new chapter in their sex-life; understanding that intimacy not intercourse forms the foundation of a loving relationship and expressing this through mutual affection.

As a stressful life-event on a par with bereavement or divorce, retirement can be a disorientating and difficult time. You may need to redress the balance in your relationship through giving each other space, communicating your feelings and providing reassurance and support to work through the difficulties and get your line of equilibrium back on track. Where physical problems such as poor general health or sexual dysfunction threaten to interfere with your sex-life, exactly the same support is needed to get through these issues together.

❝❝ Grow old along with me! The best is yet to be, the last of life, for which the first was made. Our times are in his hand who saith, 'A whole I planned, youth shows but half; Trust God: See all, nor be afraid!' " –

Robert Browning

Our relationships may have be rocked by retirement, forcing us to redefine boundaries and remark our territory at home, explore our leisure time and reevaluate our social lives, making sure we have enough space from our partner while preserving a close and intimate bond. This is a delicate balancing act and everyone drops a plate occasionally – but stick with it, the rewards are worth it.

We can only be in the right frame of mind to fix our relationship if we are being honest with ourselves when deciding what we want in retirement. This is why your 'perfect retirement picture' comprising your leisure activities, plans to return to work either paid or voluntary, part-time or full-time is so vital to enjoying the next phase. Although few people would say that they are 100% happy with every aspect of their life, the more prepared you are to engage with new experiences in retirement, including things that you may have ruled out decades ago as dull or difficult can surprise you. Who knows, I might even try golf again (that's a lie). Being receptive to new experiences is the key to personal growth at any age.

Community and your social convoy

An essential aspect of this experience is interaction with the world around us, or the 'intangible element' mentioned by Kofi Annan that keeps us going throughout our lives and props us up at difficult junctures; at times where the stress of a transition threatens our happiness. This element is our social circle; our community of friends and family. Everyone from Abraham Maslow, to Dr Phil, to the fictional Little Prince would agree that this is what keeps us going, and is the glue that holds 'the magic three' together, cementing our personal well-being.

As well as joining clubs and finding leisure being a crucial aspect of meeting people and keeping in touch with ex-colleagues, maintaining contact with people from different backgrounds and different age-groups to impart your skills and pick up useful information like what 'ROFL' stands for, or the secret to getting a high score on Angry Birds keeps our minds lively and our spirit intact.

The internet is the invisible infrastructure that supports this sense of community in the modern world by providing a medium to stay in touch with our loved ones, and explore and expand our own interests. We can express ourselves and interact with the world around us like never before; building bonds that not only replaces work but eclipses it as we rekindle old friendships and socialize with people with the same niche interests as ourselves, leading to friendship and even love in the 'real world'.

A small admission...

I admit that I might have gone off on a tangent at points and used the term sex-life as a metaphor describing more than just intercourse, sexual play or even intimacy, but as representing the self-confidence and self-belief that we take into retirement. If you have lost a long-term partner and have no intention of meeting anybody else, this shouldn't lower your expectations of finding happiness.

A study on celibacy from 1986 looked at the convent records of a group of nearly 700 nuns in later-life (an ideal group to focus on when studying celibacy) and showed that abstinence did not necessarily lead to an early death. The study also found that those with active lifestyles frequently lived into their 90s, with some even making it to three digits (I didn't really want to mention that one until near the end), but hey, there's a study for everything.

When I visited the older persons' charity, Age UK, I heard the story of a concerned son of a ninety-year-old man in a care home who wanted to have sex with the woman in the next room. "Is the lady aware of this?" The staff member asked. "Yes, she wants to have sex with him as well" he replied. "So they have both given their consent? What exactly is the problem?" Talking about these intimate details and making sex in later-life less of taboo can only be a good thing and, at its most serious, prevent these flagrant breaches of basic human needs on the grounds of ignorance.

Holding out for a telegram...

The only way is up. With the odds of making it to the magic '100' rising from 1 in 20 million to 1 in 50 for females in low-mortality nations such as Japan and Sweden, the population of centenarians is expected to rocket from 270,000 as of 2005 to more than 2.3 million in 2040, a greater proportion of people will be looking to maximize their years of healthy, active living for longer than ever by focusing on the 'magic three' and tending to their holistic personal wellbeing.

In her fabulous book on centenarians, Neenah Ellis reveals that many of her subjects held social ties and community links in very high esteem. Companionship, communication, reciprocity of feelings and affection have the power to prolong your life and will make you happy in your retirement years so start living and start loving today.

Biography

Larry Gould is a high-profile British serial entrepreneur and the holder of an Honorary Doctorate from Leeds Metropolitan University. Having built up two multi million dollar businesses with a spell of retirement in between, he knows more than most about the impact that working - and not working - can have on all of us.

It was in 1980 that Larry launched his first business, a recruitment firm employing just five staff. Over the next decade it grew to a $30 million turnover and he sold the business for a multi million dollar sum.

At that point, he decided to retire; enjoy life, develop hobbies, travel and spend time with his family. But instead of the fun-filled days he'd anticipated, Larry felt empty, directionless and bored. Even worse, despite having a devoted wife and loving family, he felt utterly unsexy.

So Larry went back to work and built from scratch another multi million dollar enterprise which is now one of the world's biggest translation and interpreting companies. Alongside this he has continued to be a tireless worker for charity, supporting a wide range of worthy causes, both through his company and as an individual.

Knowing that retirement may come along again one day, Larry has spent the past two years researching its impact. His aim has been to find out how people can deal with the loss of the structure that work brings and how they can retain their confidence and self-esteem in family and personal relationships. The result of his research is this book.

In huge demand as an interviewee and public speaker, this is Larry Gould's first non-business publication. In it, he passes on the lessons learned from his failed first retirement, now truly believing that it is possible to have a great retirement and a great sex life.